# PRAISE FOR
## *SUICIDE, COVID-19, AND KETAMINE: HOW A LITTLE KNOWN DRUG SAVES LIVES*

"It is no surprise that an increasing number of Americans have been suicidal in the last few years. What is a surprise to many is that there is a treatment that often brings immediate improvement and reduction in suicidality: Ketamine. Dr. Johnathan Edwards has dug deep into the studies, conducted his own research, then drew upon his profound compassion to get the message out. Thank you, Johnathan, for your work that improves and saves lives. And for writing a book that will do the same."

—Gavin de Becker – author of *The Gift of Fear*.

"Over the last few decades, deaths from auto accidents, many infectious diseases, and some forms of cancer have dropped considerably. Since the turn of this century, suicide mortality is up more than 30% in the U.S., despite more people getting more treatment for psychiatric disorders. This book reminds us that we need to focus our treatments specifically on reducing suicide and that ketamine is an important new treatment that can save lives."

—Thomas Insel, MD, former Director of the National Institute of Mental Health and author of *Healing: Our Path from Mental Illness to Mental Health*

"Job well done! Dr. Edwards has hit on all the key points with hard data to support, which will shed light on the current adolescent suicide pandemic of COVID-19."

—Dr. Sheldon Jacobs, Licensed Marriage &Family Therapist, and author of *48 – AN EXPERIENTIAL MEMOIR ON HOMELESSNESS.*

"This book is excellent. I have been a teacher in Las Vegas for 33 years and educate young students in suicide prevention. It has always been a problem; hopefully, this book will increase awareness and help parents prevent these very real catastrophes."

—Louie Amelburu Jr. – Director of Suicide Prevention at O'Callaghan School, Las Vegas, Nevada.

"Dr. Johnathan Edwards is not a maverick but a master clinician. He is at the forefront of those increasingly rare men and women who embody an ideal: passionate advocates for their patient's health and well-being. One hopes this extraordinary book will have a ripple effect, enlightening not only laypeople but doctors themselves. Dr. Edwards has awakened the sleeping giant that is ketamine."

—Bruce Wagner – Novelist

"We are amidst an explosion of mental illness, depression, and its successful fulfillment in suicide. Until experienced firsthand, few can grasp the miracle that ketamine can bestow."

—Joel Friedman M.D., Family Physician, Maui, Hawaii

"A well written account of a current and societally relevant analysis of our current state of mental-health. His open-minded approach to prioritizing global health is a breath of fresh air in our current environment."

—Dr. Sam Zand, Psychiatrist, and CEO of the Calm Clinic in Las Vegas, Nevada.

# SUICIDE, COVID-19, AND KETAMINE

## HOW A LITTLE KNOWN DRUG SAVES LIVES

JOHNATHAN EDWARDS, MD
Foreword by GAVIN DE BECKER

# TABLE OF CONTENTS

# DEDICATION

My parents and teachers, Bill and Susan Edwards, who gave me all what they could. To the few high school teachers who were able to see past my impatience, and my coaches in all my sports who nurtured my motivations. To Gavin De Becker, who encouraged me after our discussion about ketamine. He truly cares about human beings and the cost of suicide to society. To Kirk McKnight and Kat Thurston-Lew for their help editing this book. To Antonio Calavitta who made the final edits.

To Dr. Sam Zand, who has helped countless patients in his psychiatry clinic as well as reviewing the manuscript. To Ronn Bailey, for his invaluable support throughout the years. To Emma Chevalier, Derek Du Chesne, Dana Gentry, Louie Amelburu, Rachel Holzer, Sheldon Jacobs, Tom Insel, Dave Feifel, Joel Friedman, and everyone else to whom I owe my sincere gratitude.

Even if this book saves a single life, it's worth all our effort.

# ABOUT THE AUTHOR

Johnathan Edwards M.D. is a board-certified anesthesiologist with a key focus on treating mental-health conditions with ketamine. Dr. Edwards has provided ketamine in his practice for over 20 years. He often works with psychiatrist Dr. Sam Zand to help patients with mental-health conditions.

Dr. Edwards is the author of several books and medical papers including *The Science of the Marathon* and *Chasing Dakar* – his study of the Dakar Rally. He practices medicine in Las Vegas, Nevada, and Port Orange, Florida. Following his early career in motocross, he studied at Victor Valley Community College, the University of California at Davis, and Eastern Virginia Medical School. He later completed a year of medicine in Lyon, France.

Dr. Edwards lives most of each year in Port Orange, Florida, with his wife and their daughter. A fluent French speaker, he and his family reside part-time in Provence.

For more information:
www.johnathanedwardsmd.com or www.docedwards.com

# PREFACE

A mother losing her child to suicide is as bad as you think it is. If you have found yourself here, you, like tens of millions of others have been touched by suicide and the mental-health crisis. When most people think about suicide, they don't imagine a young child taking his or her own life. Suicide is the stuff of other people's nightmares. When it happens to you, the reality of our grief is insurmountable. No amount of therapy can help you make sense of what just happened or take away your pain. There's no going back to "OK." Time simply stops. The event continually replays in your head, leaving you wondering what you could have done differently. Certainly, getting help, of any kind, is a first step. A mental-health provider can offer therapy, medications, and support groups. Most never see it coming. Picking up on the subtle signs of mental illness only becomes apparent well after the fact. These signs are even more difficult to see in a young child.

Hayden Hunstable took his own life just four days before his thirteenth birthday. During the COVID-19 pandemic in 2020, 18 students committed suicide in Las Vegas. More than 100 adolescents jumped to their death from the Golden Gate Bridge in 2020. There were 228 U.S. police officer suicides in 2020. Then there is the isolated case of Drew Robinson, a major league baseball player who lived through his suicide attempt.

The COVID-19 crisis has been gasoline to the fire that is the existing mental-health crisis, as the lockdowns have clearly exacerbated the problem. More adults and adolescents are depressed than ever. While suicides during the lockdowns have not increased as many thought they would, the resulting increase in mental illness is undeniable. About 1 million actually go through with the act and ultimately die. Suicide is truly a hijacking of our brain telling us to end our life prematurely. What if there were a way to remove this hijacking device and grant us time to work things out so we do not want to commit suicide? Ketamine is the one drug we have available to us today that can stop suicide in its tracks. Most people have never heard of ketamine. Even those who have still probably do not know it could be used for stopping suicide. Ketamine is not the final answer in ending suicide, but it is one tool we have that can change the course. Imagine if your loved one is determined to end their life, and you could get them the help they needed. Most people would think this to be a reasonable action. If we could give ketamine to a person who is acutely suicidal, this may grant the time necessary to find the help needed to save your loved one's life. After reading this book, you will be able to more fully understand what suicide is, how to possibly prevent it, and it's devastating cost to our society. To those who say more studies are needed to know if ketamine really helps suicide and depression, I offer you this admonition before first trying the drug: if you are that person suffering from depression and suicide, the risk versus reward is clearly in favor of using ketamine now. This book brings together many different aspects of the COVID-19 crisis, the mental-health crisis, suicidality, and how ketamine can help. This book draws from many aspects of medicine and various specialties including the following: Anesthesiology, Psychiatry, Psychology, Emergency Medicine, Pain Medicine, Family Practice, and much more. This book is important for the wider interest because it addresses considerably more than just ketamine, including the mental-health crisis, the toll of suicide on our society, and the consequences we have all endured with the COVID-19 crisis. Throughout this book, you will encounter many stories about suicide, mental-health, lockdowns, and how ketamine changed the course of people's mental illness. Ketamine has been safely used for over 70 years. There are scores of publications about ketamine; about 6,500 papers exist in the Medline/PubMed database. Today, two decades later, these findings and data may be at their most important, as the world we live in continues to lose its bet to suicide.

This book is dedicated to the invisible lives lost from suicide.

# FOREWORD BY GAVIN DE BECKER, BESTSELLING AUTHOR OF *THE GIFT OF FEAR*

Every suicide ends one life – but rolls a grenade into the lives of many others. I saw that firsthand when my mother ended her life; like all family members who experience suicide, I've felt it every day since, despite 50 years having passed. The act of suicide, a tragedy usually preceded by plenty of pain, becomes the most dramatic moment in lives with plenty of drama.

Today, the use of mass lockdowns as a mitigation method for COVID-19 has many consequences unrelated to the virus: upended social order, economic destruction, job loss, poverty, anxiety, isolation from loved ones and friends, alienation, drug and alcohol abuse, depression, hopelessness. The last few items – isolation, alienation, alcohol and drugs, depression, and hopelessness – are the four horsemen of the personal apocalypse, stampeding through our society right now. Even in those pockets where actual suicides have not increased, depression, drug abuse and suicidal ideation have - dramatically.

At a low point in our society, when people need connection and companionship and community, many government plans called for Stay at Home, isolate, separate, distance, cover your face, touch no-one. When an elderly husband went to the hospital for Covid-19, he went alone. His spouse watched him taken from their home, and in too many cases, never saw him again. He died alone, and during the period that funerals were restricted, his spouse and family mourned alone. More than a million and half Americans died in hospitals in 2020 (not only from COVID-19), and most died alone.

It is no surprise that an increasing number of Americans have been suicidal in the last two years.

What is a surprise to many (but not to Dr. Johnathan Edwards) is that there is a treatment that often brings immediate improvement and reduction in suicidality: Ketamine.

Ketamine has been FDA-approved for decades and remains the anesthesia of choice for children because of its excellent safety profile. We know the dose for treatment of depression is safe because it is one-tenth the dose that's been used millions of times for anesthesiology.

As long ago as 2010, the New York Times reported:

"It has been known for several years that small doses of ketamine can relieve major depression."

Said Maggie, 53, "I woke up the next morning, and I didn't take an antidepressant for the first time in 20 years."

"I look at the cost of not using ketamine — for me it was certain death," said Dennis Hartman, 48, a businessman from Seattle.

He said that after a lifetime of severe depression, he had chosen a suicide date when he entered a clinical trial of ketamine at the National Institutes of Health two years ago. His depression lifted and since then he has gone to a clinic in New York every two months or so for infusions.

In a 2012 study published in the journal Science, the authors called ketamine "the most important discovery in half-a-century."

My life's work has been assessing and managing risk, and ketamine can reduce the risk of suicide. Ketamine is available, safe, well-tolerated, and inexpensive - yet, even though depression is among the world's leading causes of death, very few doctors know any of what you've just read here.

We all have reason to be grateful that Johnathan Edwards wrote this important book. He dug deep into the studies, conducted his own research, then drew upon his profound compassion to get the message out - a message that will help far more than just his own patients. Rather than merely study the sad statistics, Dr. Edwards committed to help those who need never become statistics at all.

Thank you, Johnathan, for your work that improves and saves lives. And for writing a book that will do the same.

Gavin de Becker

# FOREWORD
# BY DR. SAM ZAND

Why does one commit suicide? What kind of contributing factors need to coalesce to bring someone to this life-ending decision? To most, the thought is terrifying, and comprehension impossible. For others, attempting suicide is the only answer remaining to squelch their anguish. For about two people per hour, it's the last worldly decision they'll ever make. Recent unfortunate suicides include beloved NFL superstar Junior Seau or actor Robin Williams.

My psychiatry training at Johns Hopkins University taught me the question persists with no definitive answer. Suicidality cannot be measured, blood tested, or imaged. The field of psychiatry is left to treat an illness not fully understood. In my psychiatry practice, looking at mental illness through the lens of one's biological, psychological, social, and spiritual factors help me better understand suicidality.

A dark, self-loathing psychological perspective is required to bring a person to extreme measures. Our life experiences, traumas, emotional conflicts, and stories sculpt our psyche. If someone is ready for suicide, their thought processes have hit a *cul-de-sac*—which is French for "dead-end." Rigid thought patterns inhibit us from reaching out for help. Our daily environment, habits, stressors, and relationships strongly influence us. Consider what social distancing does to someone already practicing isolative and self-deprecating behaviors.

The spiritual elements of life include questions like – what's the point of all this? Why are we here? What happens after we pass? There are no correct answers here. Those who have misaligned their spiritual truths find it harder to discover a sense of peace and empowerment. Life lacks significance for those without purpose, appreciation, or a sense of enjoyment.

The COVID-19 pandemic has been a polarizing and revealing time for humanity. I observed the anxious develop more worry, the depressed becoming more isolated, and mood lability growing more volatile. The agoraphobics loved social distancing, and OCD patients felt both frightened and vindicated. Substance abuse skyrocketed. The social inequities, fear, financial stress, relationships, mental illness were all apparent. I saw weight gain from sedentary lifestyles. Patients questioned every cough, worrying about contamination. The media exacerbated fears while, political and racial tensions continuously intensified. Lack of social outlets and human connection afflicted the masses. We all confronted death simultaneously. This worldwide pandemic did that.

On the positive side, the world could breathe again. In March 2020, we observed the regeneration of bioluminescent organisms in contaminated beaches. As industry halted, the earth began to glow again. Noise levels on seismic stations dropped in every city in the world, allowing us to see through the blur of human impact.

I managed the case of Drew Robinson, who you will read about in the first chapter. He survived his self-inflicted gunshot wound to the head during the lockdowns. He was neurologically and physically healthy, but the concealed self-hatred, combined with social isolation, created a spiritual cul-de-sac for Drew. His solution was suicide, but luckily the universe had bigger plans for him. Indeed, not everyone is so lucky. Dr. Edwards tells the story of Drew Robinson, of course, with his permission.

What more can be done? Serendipitously, a new medication for major depression with suicidal thoughts was cleared by the FDA: ketamine. Specifically, ketamine under the name Spravato. Ketamine affects the totality of our bio-psycho-social and spiritual health. Improving brain chemistry, resetting emotional thought processes, and most importantly, unlocking a spiritual perspective on life. No other currently available drug is capable of stopping suicidal ideation the way that ketamine does. Maybe that will change with the advent of psilocybin and other medications.

Everyone is looking for the magic pill. It probably doesn't exist, but we all have the capability of unlocking the healing powers within. Neuroplasticity is essential, and ketamine helps us access the ability to form new and more flexible neural circuitry.

If we apply the lessons that the COVID-19 crisis has taught us about mental-health, we can undo some of the anxiety, depression, fear, insomnia, and substance abuse. If we look even further, we might better understand how to save the invisible lives lost to suicide. Inspired minds like Dr. Edwards will help lead us down that road.

Sam Zand D.O., Psychiatrist and CEO of The Calm Clinic, Las Vegas, Nevada.

# PART ONE: THE PROBLEM

# CHAPTER ONE:
## WHY A BOOK ABOUT SUICIDE, COVID-19, AND KETAMINE?

*"All it takes is one small change on the
earth to make a world of difference."*
—Anonymous

Why? These topics are more interrelated than you might think. The World Health Organization (WHO) estimates that 800,000 people die from suicide each year, which represents a global mortality rate of one death every 40 seconds. It is predicted that this rate of death will increase to one every 20 seconds. In the U.S., suicide is a serious problem, with 1.2 million suicide attempts taking the lives of over 40,000 people each year, similar to the number of deaths from automobile accidents. Did you know that more Americans have died from suicide than during all wars combined since Vietnam? And globally, suicide kills more than a million people each year. Equally, the COVID-19 pandemic has taken millions of lives. But have you wondered about the long-term unintended consequences of COVID-19? We are not talking about medical complications like respiratory, cardiac, or kidney diseases. Rather, the deluge of mental-health problems resulting from the pandemic. Of course, depression, suicide and drug overdoses have been a problem since long before the pandemic. But COVID-19 has made the situation worse: it is more of a crisis than a pandemic, and it's arguable that we have portrayed the actual disease as worse than it is while ignoring the many secondary consequences. Lockdowns have fueled a litany of tragedies in addition to the suicides, drug overdoses, heightened crime, starvation, financial ruin, and much more.

The COVID-19 crisis paralyzed the world in 2020. The COVID-19 pandemic comprises two crises - the mortality from the SARS-COVID-2 virus, and the deaths resulting from the unintended consequences of the lockdowns. Adolescent and adult mental illness have skyrocketed, and the tsunami of post-traumatic stress, depression, and suicides will follow. Death from suicide is an inconvenient truth of the COVID-19 crisis. The mental-health consequences will persist long after the COVID-19 pandemic ends. Stay-at-home orders were challenging for some families with child abuse, domestic violence, and drug overdoses becoming everyday occurrences. For many, COVID-19 is the most imminent thing on earth, if not the only thing. Millions have lost their jobs, homes, and businesses, while gun, drug, and alcohol sales continue to rise.

In 2020, 18 Las Vegas school children took their lives. As if rubbing salt in the wound, these lockdowns have removed many traditional mental-health resources. In 2020, more police officers died by their own guns than in the line of duty. Because of the lockdowns, we expect millions of people will die of hunger and postponed medical treatments, a potential outcome that, unfortunately, has developed less notice. The result is a "perfect storm" of suicides and drug overdose deaths.

Mental-health practitioners are employing everything, including telemedicine, to help people battle this threat. Frontline health care workers are under huge stress, and some of these workers have also committed suicide. Fear, self-isolation, and social distancing exacerbate the detrimental effects on people with and without mental-illness. Suicide and depression are also increasing because of the stigma towards individuals with COVID-19 and their families. Suicide is subtle, and the decision to take your own life is often impulsive. The treatment of suicide and depression is complex, with current medications taking weeks or months to work. When a loved one commits suicide, they leave many unanswered questions; constant thoughts of "what" and "why," permeate the minds of those left behind.

In reality, we do not have many treatments for suicide. But there is one drug that is capable of stopping suicide: ketamine. Few are aware that this decades-old anesthetic and party drug might save your loved one's or even your life. You might well be wondering how it can be a game-changer for treating suicide, PTSD, and depression. Most psychiatrists and other mental-health professionals will attest that few medications can effectively treat suicide or treatment-resistant depression. However, we have years of research showing that ketamine can rapidly stop suicidal ideation, buying precious time to seek help. The military uses ketamine to help war veterans recover from PTSD. Additionally, Intensive Care Unit specialists are using ketamine to treat the out-of-control inflammation that kills so many afflicted with COVID-19. Ketamine is a legitimate path to treat certain mental disorders. Simply said, ketamine works. If your loved one was suicidal, would you suggest trying ketamine? Or use it yourself?

The following story is about professional baseball player, Drew Robinson, and his attempted suicide during the lockdown, and his path to choosing life.

## Case: Drew Robinson

On the morning of April 16th, 2020, professional baseball player, Drew Robinson sat at his kitchen table, finishing a note to his family explaining why he was going to end his life. This young man recently signed a major league baseball contract with the San Francisco Giants and should have felt on top of the world. Suicide knows no boundaries. Like everyone else, being confined by the lockdowns during the COVID-19 crisis for over a month undoubtedly led him closer to the decision. He hated his life; even worse, he hated that no one knew how much he hated his life. Hiding his hate and hopelessness, Drew was living his dream but still wanted to die.

Around 5 p.m., everything came together: a handgun, a neatly-placed letter, a clean house, and some whiskey. He drove to the park in his truck. However, he decided he did not want to die in his truck, so he returned home. Three hours later, alone on his couch, he reached for his gun on the coffee table then discharged a bullet against his right temple.

Over the next 20 hours, he would come to realize his suicide was the beginning of another story. Shortly after the gunshot, Drew looked around, confused that he was still conscious. Disappointed as one could be who wanted to commit suicide, he laid down on the ground and waited to die. Thirty minutes passed. He held a rag to his head, as one would instinctively do to cover their wounds. It did not hurt. He took a shower, then fell and lay on the bathroom floor. Later, he found himself lying in his bed. He even tried to brush his teeth. He remembered thinking to himself how ridiculous it all was. He had a hole in his head and he was brushing his teeth. Four hours after he pulled the trigger, he was alive but still planned to let himself bleed to death.

The following day, he woke up in pain, to the sound of his phone buzzing. He went to the kitchen, drank some water, and took a Tylenol. The gun was still on the coffee table, but he grabbed his phone instead. He stared at his reflection in the bathroom mirror. He did not recognize his face. He again, saw his gun on the coffee table and thought about baseball. He wondered, "*Could I play with one eye?*" He wondered if thinking about the future meant he was trying to survive.

*That single Tylenol pill. W*as it some kind of subconscious message that he wanted to live? Drew looked at his phone and saw a text from his friend Darryl who had come over to work out in his gym. In the afternoon, Drew returned to the couch where it all started, both the gun and his cell phone on the coffee table. Holding the gun to his head a second time, he instead dialed 911 and asked for an ambulance.

It was 3:44 p.m. when Drew called 911, wondering how on earth he was still alive.

"I need an ambulance," he said. "I tried to commit suicide last night, and I made it through. I think I detached my eye, maybe. I can't open it, and I have a huge hole in my head, and I'm in a lot of pain."

"What'd you do?" the dispatcher asked.

"I shot myself in the head," Drew said.

Police in the area rushed to his house.

At 3:51 p.m., police kicked down the front door. They were afraid this might be an ambush. A guy shoots himself in the head and lives for 20 hours?

At 3:52 p.m., the officer asked: "Why'd you shoot yourself?" Drew replied in a whisper: "Because I hate myself."

At 3:53 p.m., an ambulance arrived and transported Drew to the UMC Trauma Center.

At 4 p.m., the police officer shook his head and said what everyone else was thinking: "That's crazy that he's still alive."

How did Drew live for nearly 24 hours with a gunshot wound to his head? And without medical attention? Few survive self-inflicted gunshot wounds to the head like this. The American construction worker, Phineas Gage, survived an iron rod driven through his head. However, Gage's friends remarked that he was "no longer Gage." Drew was lucky. He emerged from his experience better, with a renewed purpose, clarity, and confidence.

Drew's right eye was beyond repair. The human eye is a remarkably resilient structure that is surrounded by bones, muscles, and fat. The orbital cavity provides ample protection from everyday life, but not from a 9 mm bullet traveling at Mach speed. The fracture in his frontal sinus caused the fluid from his brain to leak, posing a significant infection risk. The bullet missed the major arteries, his left orbital floor, and exited above his left cheekbone.

The doctors had to reconstruct Drew's face. The first procedure was the surgery to save his right eyelid. The second was to reconstruct the eye orbit and to return most of the symmetry to his face. The third was to fix the fracture in his sinuses and stop the leakage of cerebrospinal fluid, which, if left untreated, could have led to meningitis, brain abscesses, chronic headaches, and death. The final and fourth surgery was an enucleation, the removal of Drew's right eye. He lost his senses of taste and smell after the surgeries.

Life is unrelenting. Today, Drew knows mental-health issues are challenging to talk about. Regardless, he wants to share his experience to others that mental illness is winnable. He feels he was supposed to go through a suicide attempt.

"*I shot myself*" he says. "*But I killed my ego. I'm free now.*"

Drew does not glorify what happened. He knows he should be dead. Instead, he is focused on fixing himself and his surrounding relationships while maintaining a professional baseball career. He prefers to not wear his eye prosthesis to show the world what he did and have more opportunities to share his experiences with the world. Drew believes that "I was supposed to tell a story." When Drew eventually spoke with his brother Chad, he repeated, "*I'm meant to be alive, Chad. I'm meant to be alive. I'm meant to be alive. I'm here for a reason. I want to tell the world what happened so I can heal, and maybe I can help others heal, too.*"

Drew explains, "*how can I go through this and not find a way to try to help other people?"* To have this happen and just move on with my life the way I was before? There's no way. This was an enormous sign. A huge, painful sign that I'm supposed to help people get through something that they don't think is winnable."

The reasons leading up to Drew's decision to attempt suicide are apparent if you study his family history. When Drew's parents, Renee and Darryl, were divorcing, it devastated him. After the divorce, the Robinson family splintered. The boys went to live with Darryl while his sister Britney stayed with Renee. They found common ground in one place: the baseball field. He remembers asking himself questions, *"Is there something wrong with me? Why is Mom so mad at me? What did I do?"* The Robinsons didn't discuss those sorts of things. They just lived one day to the next. The family never handled emotions well, causing a lot of stress and internal struggles. "I think we all had this idea of a perfect family and things like that. When it didn't live up to that, we questioned everything we were doing."

Drew's brother, Chad, was drafted to the Milwaukee Brewers in 2006, setting a near-impossible standard in Drew's mind. Drew became obsessed with an image of perfection. He made varsity at Silverado High School as a freshman and became the best player there since his brother. Professional sports put tremendous pressure on Drew. There were the 4:30 AM wake-up calls for workouts, long bus rides, injuries, and drug testing. Being a professional baseball player isn't only about playing baseball better than everyone else. It is an accelerated adulthood for an 18-year-old paying bills, managing disappointment, navigating politics, forging relationships, and figuring out how to live in a universe designed to weed out the weak.

Drew's life seemed ideal on the surface: he had a professional baseball contract, family support, and a fiancée. In spite of all these positives, Drew could not stop hating himself. Despite powerful support from his fiancée, Daiana, he broke off the relationship abruptly. She thought they were going to get married, and just like that, it was over. Drew was stuck in a rut with never-ending questions in his mind:

*"Why does everything suck? Why is this happening to me? Is there something I'm doing wrong? Why can't you just be honest with everyone and let them know how much you hate yourself? Is it even worth it? Is my life even worth it?"*

His self-doubt paralyzed his life. He never felt like he belonged. The voice in his head grew louder. Drew grew more depressed. His suicidal ideation intensified. Understanding that he needed help, he saw a therapist and read self-development books. He wanted to see himself the way he perceived everyone else saw themselves. But the self-doubt compounded into another question:

*"Who would care if I'm gone?"*

When no answer came, he planned his suicide. Drew visited a gun range in the Phoenix area. Each shot birthed another question.

*"Could this be a real possibility? How would I even do it? Where would I do it? No,* Drew then told himself. *No! That's too extreme. Just talk to someone and get some help. We can do it. Just talk to someone. Find anyone, even if it's a surface-level conversation. Nobody wants to hear it. Nobody needs to hear it."*

He continued therapy sessions, but they didn't rid him of his worst thoughts. His frustration with himself multiplied. He was trying to embrace his vulnerability, but even if Daiana and others saw progress, he saw stasis. He began to feel he wasn't good enough for her and hated himself. He called off the wedding.

Then COVID-19 shut down the baseball world in March. Drew returned to Las Vegas, to an empty house, loneliness, and not knowing who he was anymore. A week later, he purchased a gun and returned on March 30th to pick it up. He had none of those surface-level conversations or light-hearted camaraderie to sway his resolve. Drew could no longer meet with friends or go to the stadium. He was just alone with the negative thoughts which had built up over two decades.

The days seemed to last forever. Friends checked in with Drew, wanting to plan something for his 28th birthday on April 20th. He ignored them. On April 13th, Drew met with a woman who had a litter of puppies. He petted and cuddled one. Then a heavy feeling weighed down on him. "*Sorry,*" he told the woman. "*I can't take this dog.*" He left hurriedly, noticing the confused look on the woman's face. "*She had no idea,*" Drew remembers. "*How could she? I couldn't take the dog because I was planning on killing myself.*"

Survivors of suicide attempts, particularly ones as violent as Drew's, have a wide range of outcomes. The combination of physical and mental trauma typically requires a reset of the body and mind that takes years. When he emerged from anesthesia after the initial surgery, Drew said how he felt love for the blanket warming him, for each breath that filled his lungs, and for his family. Never had he felt compelled to say he loved them. Saying "I love you" was just a habit, what you're supposed to say. Drew was determined that his "after" was going to be different from his "before."

"I never will hold back from asking or telling someone, even if it's something simple," Drew says. "*Hey, this little thing's annoying me today.* Just tell them. They want to hear it. People who love you want to hear it, and if you don't have people who love you, therapists want to hear it. People want to help you. So many people in this world will help anyone go through these things. It might be a specific situation that makes you feel you're alone, but you're never alone. "*Think about it. Not everyone can do it. So, if not everyone can do it, but some people can, that's just like having a strength. Hey, I reached out to someone today, I told him how I felt, and I felt really good. Why can't that be a strength?*"

Drew had found that strength emerging from those 20 dark hours, from the shadowy details he somehow remembered when he reconsidered his family and the idea of coming back to play baseball, not just to see if he could, but to show others what is possible.

Cleaning Drew's house after the suicide attempt was something parents should never have to experience. They were entering through the garage and unprepared for what they saw. His mother, Britney looked up the phone numbers of hazmat cleaners.

"*No,*" Darryl responded. "*We're cleaning it.*" No way was he going to let a stranger into the house to see the remnants of his son's worst moment. Darryl scoured the walls, while Chad, wiped the floors and Britney handled the linens. She borrowed an industrial carpet cleaner from her office. They were on their hands and knees, knowing they couldn't erase reality, but determined to scrub as much of it away as possible.

Drew needed to experience the house where he almost died. He walked toward the couch and sat in the same spot where he shot himself.

"*I wanted to feel it again,*" he says. "*I wanted to feel the power, not the bad side. I'm still here.*" When Daiana, Darryl, Britney, and

Chad visited him at the house that night, he walked them through the 20 hours. They were speechless. Drew could see the distress on their faces. "No one understands how I made it through," he says. "No one has to." He said they could ask him anything.

"They each wanted to know, "what could we have done?"

*Nothing. It was my responsibility, not yours.*

"How come we didn't know?"

*Because I was good at hiding my sadness.*

"Why did you do it?"

Drew didn't have a good response to this one. He remembered what he told the police officer: *I hate myself.* Sometimes that's all it takes.

Suicide attempts leave behind the sort of choppy wake that can waylay even a person who has had years of therapy and proper medication. People who attempt suicide often try it again until they succeed. "I don't have it all figured out, but I'm working on it," Drew says. "It's not something that you just achieve. You don't just achieve self-growth. You don't get to a point where you just have it, and you don't have to work at it again. You don't get to a point, Oh, I'm happy today. That's it. I'm going to be happy for the rest of my life. It's the same way in the opposite. I had a rough day. That doesn't mean the rest of your life is going to suck."

Drew follows a daily regimen. He typically wakes before his alarm. He plays with his dogs Ellie and Brodi and then goes into the kitchen, drinks a jug of water, and meditates for 20 minutes. He then goes to the gym, comes back to eat breakfast, then goes to the office. One day at a time.

In the afternoon, Drew tries to make at least three phone calls to connect, catch up, ask questions, talk about how he's doing. He'll workout again, either in his gym or at the batting cages, before returning home to listen to music, watch TV, or spend time with his family. Before bed, Drew does some journaling. Sometimes he'll write a whole page, and sometimes just a sentence. Either way, every entry ends with the same eight words:

I LOVE MYSELF, AND I LOVE MY LIFE!!

Drew's mission in life has changed substantially. After leaving the hospital, Drew remained in contact with the Giants' management. He sent them pictures and videos of himself in the gym and on the field. The Giants psychologist put pieces of tape with the names of each nurse at UMC hospital on Drew's jersey on National Front-Line Workers' Day. September 10th is World Suicide Prevention Day, and Drew asked if he could speak to his teammates the Giants' players and staff. Playing baseball was important, but if Drew was going to help others, he needed to tell his story. The Giants welcomed the idea. He arrived at Oracle Park wearing a mask with a Giants logo, and no eye prosthesis. The players, coaches, and other staff gathered outside. Drew spoke with the microphone and said, "First, I just want to say thank you for everything." "What I've been going through the last couple of months has been the most powerful experience in the most positive way. The lessons I've learned from what I've gone through is something I want to share."

"On April 16th, around 8 p.m., I attempted suicide and shot myself in the head. A day later, April 17th, around 4 p.m., I dialed 911 myself in an attempt to have my life saved. Later that night, not only was my life saved, but it was reborn and restarted."

Drew spoke about the importance of talking, the need for others, and his intention of giving baseball another shot. He saw people crying. Some were undoubtedly thinking of family or friends lost to suicide.

In November, a familiar feeling seized Drew. Something was off. It started with a skipped workout, then a missed meditation session and journal entry. The pressures of his new routine and the new expectations he had set were getting to him. His mind racing, Drew told himself he was being lazy and he wasn't putting in the work to stay healthy. *If I can't do the work, why would I deserve happiness? If I can't even do enough to earn happiness, what's the point?"* He didn't leave his room for a day. One day turned into two, and then three. His negative self-talk sounded like the Drew "before," not the Drew "after." "*I just felt like the world was ending,*" he says. "I had my first passive suicidal thought, which scared me: I wish I'd been successful." Sticking to his daily routine, continuing to see his therapist Dr. Zand, and belief in mission certainly helped him through this difficult period.

Drew will never know exactly what caused him to call 911 that day, but the clues have always been there. In the hours before he pulled the trigger, and throughout those 20 hours that followed, his thoughts constantly converged on his family and his then fiancée Daiana. Reminders of April 16th now surround him. Drew kept the shorts he was wearing, the blood-soaked towel, and the note he wrote to his family. His parents removed the plank of wood where the bullet had lodged and made it into a necklace for him.

Today, Drew Robinson is still playing baseball. He is also forming a foundation to raise awareness for suicide prevention with a social media platform called the BetterU.Foundation, along with psychiatrist, Dr. Sam Zand, and Hollywood actor and entrepreneur, Derek Du Chesne. Drew interacts with his therapists weekly and has undergone an in-office ketamine treatment. He understands antidepressants are a treatment to balance his brain. He optimizes his sleep and exercise and monitors his nutrition. With the help and encouragement of right fielder and former Giant, Hunter Pence, he meditates. Drew occasionally works construction with his dad to earn extra cash and occupy his time. Whatever it takes to make sure the words, "I love myself, and I love my life" make it into his daily journal entry.

Source: Personal interview with Drew Robinson and adapted from ESPN article, San Francisco Giants outfielder Drew Robinson remarkable second act. May 11th, 2020. Jeff Passan on ESPN E:60 Preview

# CHAPTER TWO:
## THE UNINTENDED CONSEQUENCES OF SUICIDE AND LOCKDOWNS

*"A litany of tragedies from lockdowns, suicide,*
*murder, drug overdoses, starvation. But*
*apparently, COVID-19 is the most important*
*thing on earth, if not the only thing."*
—Gavin de Becker

On November 11th, 2020, Nevada Governor Steve Sisolak revealed that another child, this one 9-years-old, in the Clark County School District had committed suicide the prior evening. In October that year, more people in Japan died from suicide than from all the country's COVID-19 deaths in 2020 combined. Sixteen military veterans commit suicide each day. The COVID-19 crisis and the accompanying mental-health crisis are global problems that will inevitably require global solutions.

No one knew what to expect in early 2020. As the SARS-COV-2 virus was taking over China, we watched in denial as the virus quickly spread worldwide. The world was not ready for the results nor the decisions that would be made. Desperately trying to find ways of slowing the spread, governments told us we needed to keep distant from each other, wear masks, and stay indoors.

The global spread of COVID-19 virus led to major government policy responses called non-pharmaceutical interventions (NPI) in order to reduce deaths and prevent overloading the health care system. Then governments instituted "most-restrictive non-pharmaceutical policies" (mrNPI), which were called lockdowns. Early adoption of lockdowns occurred in 2020 when substantial uncertainty about the virus existed and in areas where the health care systems were overwhelmed. While lockdowns may be conceptually sound, they are less effective in practice. Lockdowns have removed many of the mental-health resources traditionally used to cope with stress. The harmful effects of lockdowns include: starvation, missed school days, opioid-related deaths, missed vaccinations, increase in non-COVID diseases, domestic abuse, economic consequences, cancer and cardiovascular deaths, mental-health disease, and suicidality. Compare the epidemic spread in places that implemented strict lockdowns to places that implemented less restrictive lockdown measures. Many studies failed to find strong evidence supporting lockdowns that included stay-at-home orders and business and school closures.

Lockdowns costed millions their jobs, homes, and businesses, with some families touching poverty for the first time. Adding in the political stress of the elections and the race riots sparked by the killing of George Floyd and others; these problems compound the mental-health crisis. In the face of all this, COVID-19's impact on suicide, though significant, is surprisingly, still, mostly unknown.

The current situation is overburdening practitioners because of the unprecedented rise in mental sickness. Telemedicine is helping by allowing mental-health professionals to provide psychotherapy and prescribe medicine all from a computer. Although video consultations ease some problems associated with the lockdowns, there are not enough providers to treat everyone.

Seven million children depend on the school system to meet their physical and psychological health needs, but schools have been closed during lockdowns. Public health measures and the World Health Organization (WHO) normally advise to keep schools open during a pandemic, but because of the fear and politicization around opening schools, most remained closed. The result was an uptick in depression and suicidal ideation. In one tragic case, a 7-year-old child was a victim.

When the complete history of COVID-19 is recorded, Harvard University Historian David Jones suggests, *"we may learn that we have been at much greater risk of exaggerated fears and misplaced priorities."* They will show some things we did right, and many actions and policies we got wrong. The COVID-19 pandemic resulted in many unfounded overreactions with long-term consequences. For many, the number of positive daily infection cases, hospitalizations, and deaths were the statistics which filled our daily news feeds. Certainly, some reaction to the COVID-19 pandemic is better than no reaction at all. But our misproportioned emphasis led people to focus on the 3 percent mortality and not the 97 percent recovery rate. Furthermore, all one has to do is look at the European Morbidity and Mortality data to realize that 80 percent of COVID-19 deaths result from 0.6 percent of the population, sick elderly adults.

As COVID-19 became a global outbreak, media coverage spread fear, anxiety, superstition, cognitive dissonance, and conspiracy theories. Enforced mask wearing, physical distancing, and emotional deprivation generated fear, hopelessness, and self-isolation. People in crisis were avoiding hospitals, and public measures were being compromised by both hysteria and denial. The social effects of banning religious ceremonies, funerals, and weddings had a tremendous impact on individuals and families alike.

Irresponsible media reporting and repeated stories about the COVID-19 crisis increased fears and heightened the risk of mental illness. Some media networks encouraged reporting that brought about the most sensationalist headlines, to garner the most views and, with them, profits. We should never forget that news outlets are profit-driven enterprises. We should not be dependent on them for facts concerning life and death issues. Listening to the chorus of 24-7 news, one might even think that our biggest problem is that COVID-19 is a hoax, or just a political tool. The increasing public understanding of the virus hasn't helped the pandemic either. Genuine concerns about the conflicting advice with regard to preventative measures and their relative costs to society raised many questions to the efficacy of lockdowns.

Lockdown fatigue is not a denial of the pandemic's significance or moral failures, rather it is human, natural, and predictable. People who have mostly spent the year complying with the confusing, changing, and often irrational guidance should not be levied as denialists. They need guidance because amid a pandemic, fear and hysteria occur simultaneously. Students are becoming anxious about their prospects when they finish school. Increased domestic violence and alcohol abuse are becoming the norm. With gun sales exploding, firearms are non-coincidentally associated with about 50 percent of suicides. Accessible firearms, medications, pesticides, and other means of suicide are being stockpiled in homes, not only enabling the decision but practically expediting the process.

Patients with psychiatric disorders experience worsening symptoms, while others are developing mental-health problems such as depression, anxiety, and PTSD, which all potentially lead to an increased risk of suicidal behavior. Front line health care workers need extra support. They are regularly working with dying patients and those that are unable to cope, consider committing suicide themselves.

Fear, self-isolation, and physical distancing exacerbate the adverse effects of the pandemic on people with and without mental illness. Loss of employment and financial stresses are well-known risk factors for suicide. The consequences are increased mental-health care workloads and adapting to alternative ways of working. Another hindrance created by these "alternative approaches" is the reduction of proximity, and, with it, interaction. Historically, mental-health clinics have been designed for face-to-face care. Currently, services are delivered via Zoom, video calls or telephone.

The pandemic has affected everyone, not only those suffering from mental-health problems. Understanding where everyone's priorities lie is difficult, but it is not a stretch to say that through misinformation and negative energies, our priorities have been hijacked during this pandemic. In a metaphysical sense, the waves of the pandemic are like the energies of the ocean. The energy of the ocean comes from the sheer mass of the water, which moves the waves. The energy of panic and fear moves through our bodies, affecting everyone. To some, these energies may feel like an unpleasant breeze, while, to others, they seem like a category 5 hurricane.

Denial of the reality in front of us delivers an interesting and beguiling effect. Those who believe the COVID-19 crisis is the only valued object of our attention are perhaps overlooking the multitude of suicides and drug overdoses. This prevents appropriate action to decrease these unfortunate statistics.

As humans, we do not have any predators, we only have ourselves to fear. Humans are the only species of animals that ever commits suicide, and about two thousand do so each day. People who commit suicide come from all walks of life - the wealthy, the working-class adults, and the poor. Suicides are often called "senseless," but there are many reasons people become depressed and take their own lives. Blaming suicides on the COVID-19 crisis seems straightforward but suicide has always been prevalent. The suicide rate has been increasing for nearly 30 years and is the tenth leading cause of death in the U.S. The rate rises and falls with pandemics and financial crises. People in suicidal crises require complex and unique care. Suicide risk and depression are increased because of the stigma towards individuals with COVID-19 and their families. The effects are worse in poor socioeconomic areas, since inadequate welfare also compounds economic adversity.

Many do not seek help, fearing they will encounter overwhelmed services or possibly catch the virus. Many suicides are impulsive and preventable. Predicting human behavior is complex and people often do things "out of the blue." Over 50 percent of all those who attempt suicide have no history of a mental-health disorder. When we are alone, afraid, and feel all hope is lost, fear hijacks our minds and controls our actions.

Individually, it seems the solution to the COVID-19 crisis will come from within, because one of the most overlooked resources is intuition. Gavin de Becker's book, *The Gift of Fear*, perfectly illustrates intuition's true meaning and value. Intuition will save you and your loved ones from the wretches of depression and suicide. Western society favors logical, grounded, explainable thought processes that end in supportable explanations: but, intuition may save your child or even your *own life*. Perhaps if the parents of the children in the Las Vegas suicide crisis would have trusted their intuition when they observed the subtle signs of mental illness or the possibility that a child could take his / her own life, it's possible that a young child could have received the help needed before their fatal decision.

Some prefer to remain in the comfortable illusion that adolescent suicide is rare. Life's highest stakes questions can be answered. What could I have done to get my loved one help? What resources were available to redirect the path? How can I keep my loved one safer? Neither privilege nor poverty can keep the negative energies of the COVID-19 crisis away or offer protection from suicide. We intently watch the news reports of the bodies from the COVID-19 virus being carried away, but no one is watching nor reporting those who die by suicide in response to affliction by the effects of the same virus.

Bringing these issues into the conversation will allow action to prevent our loved ones and fellow human beings suffering from depression and suicide. We've presented these facts about the frequency of death for a reason: to increase the likelihood you believe we can do something more about our loved ones and fellow human beings suffering from depression and suicide. This book is for all the "invisible lives" lost in this COVID-19 crisis. By the end of this book, I ensure that you will be better able to answer these questions and more. As we mentioned in Chapter One, one modality is proven effective against suicidal ideation, and very few people are talking about it - the decades-old medication called ketamine. Ketamine, mostly known as a recreational drug in party circles, can arrest suicidal ideation. We have no other medication that can accomplish this yet, few know or ever ask about ketamine treatments.

The following is a story from Dr. Gerald Grass's clinic about suicide and how ketamine can stop suicidal ideation.

## Case: Olive

Olive is typical of many patients with a severe history of depression and suicidal ideation. By age 15, doctors diagnosed Olive with generalized anxiety disorder, panic disorder, PTSD, and bipolar disorder. She went through all the traditional approaches with psychiatrists and psychologists to treat her psychiatric conditions such as cognitive-behavioral therapy, psychotherapy, counseling, meditation, mindfulness, and yoga. Taking several medications like Prozac, Celexa, Zoloft, Lexapro, Effexor and many others with little effect, she often felt hopeless and spent much of her time alone, crying and sad. For her, depression was cancer for her soul and hell for her spirit. By age 27, she had fought the severity of her illness, but a residual depression and irritability lingered.

As time continued, Olive's outlook darkened until she felt as though her life was not worth living. She decided that suicide was her only option. Unable to take her own life by conventional means, she planned to travel to the Netherlands for an assisted suicide. She painted a picture of "Autumn Lake," which depicted her thoughts of what heaven would look like. She wanted her mother to envision her in this lake after she was gone.

A doctor suggested Olive try ketamine. However, Olive had already arranged her assisted suicide. On the very day she was to leave for the Netherlands, Olive decided to try the ketamine treatments. Under the direction of Dr. Gerald Grass, she underwent multiple ketamine infusions and was no longer suicidal. After three ketamine infusions over three days, Olive's suicidal ideation was gone, along with her depression and anxiety.

After the ketamine treatments, she describes her depression as being replaced with joy, and anxiety with tranquility. She describes her brain as calm and her heart was filled with happiness and love. Olive's renewed passion for life has given her a second chance. She describes moving forward with confidence, knowing if her symptoms return, she can go back to the ketamine treatments. In short, Olive got her life back thanks to ketamine.

Source: Gerald Grass clinic

# CHAPTER THREE:
## THERE'S MORE THAN COVID-19 KILLING PEOPLE

Alice Laughed: *"There's no use trying,"* she
said, *"one can't believe impossible things."*
—Lewis Carroll, *Alice in Wonderland*

What has happened with COVID-19 has happened, and the decisions made will shape us for years to come. Humankind is facing an unprecedented crisis. COVID-19 is a new, mutated, coronavirus that is more deadly than most forms of influenza (at least in the elderly).

Legitimate research estimates that 100 million deaths worldwide are expected from starvation and postponed medical treatments by 2022; and thousands of more deaths from suicides and drug overdoses.

Countries are experiencing second, third, and fourth waves of COVID-19, along with more lockdowns and restrictions to daily life. Many hospital systems are being pushed to the brink. The COVID-19 virus has spread to over 200 countries; as of July 2021, the global cases were 185,668,819. COVID-19 deaths had reached 4,013,764 people globally and 621,681 in the United States. The number of "non-COVID" deaths from suicide and drug overdoses is only just being realized. Historically, suicide rates always increase with a pandemic (see box: Previous Epidemics and Suicide).

How deadly is COVID-19? However, it is difficult to assess because of the variation in death rates reported in different countries. For example, England reported a 3 percent risk of dying from COVID-19, while Singapore reported a 0.02 percent risk. John Ioannidis, an influential figure in the world of medical research, estimated the fatality rate to be about 0.20 percent. If you get COVID-19 in England versus elsewhere, you are one hundred and fifty times more likely to die. To put this in perspective, so far, it seems to be equivalent to a severe flu pandemic (see the avian flu pandemics of the 1950s). The Spanish flu had a mortality rate of about 2.5 percent, which is about 14 times more deadly than COVID-19. Several countries implemented measures to contain the spread, which initially involved quarantining travelers coming from areas of the world known to be infected.

## A Timeline of the COVID-19 Crisis

**November 2019**. The first COVID-19 cases are reported in Wuhan, China. Three researchers from China's Wuhan Institute of Virology became sick enough to seek hospital care.

**December 2019**. Hundreds of people are flying out of China worldwide, increasing the spread of COVID-19.

**January 2020**. The World Health Organization (WHO) debated the laboratory origins of what would become the COVID-19 pandemic. Chinese health officials claimed there had been no human transmission of the novel coronavirus within China. The virus was found within Brazilian sewers as early as November 2019. On January 21st, the U.S. confirms its first COVID-19 case. According to German intelligence resources (Der Spiegel), WHO director Tedros received communication from Chairman Xi of China urging him to delay the warning that person-to-person transmission of the coronavirus has taken place. On January 23rd, WHO director Tedros issues a statement that the novel coronavirus is a regional problem. Wuhan first goes into lockdown in late January, and the WHO issues a Global Health Emergency. Human-to-human transmission is quickly spreading. The WHO declares COVID-19 to be a "public health emergency" on January 30th, 2020, acknowledging that the virus had already spread, albeit in small numbers, across the globe. On January 31st, former President Trump restricts all travel to China. A record number of U.S. police officers died by suicide in 2019; approximately twenty-five percent were veterans with at least 20 years of service.

**February 2020**. Tedros announces that international travel and trade can continue. In February, global air travel is restricted, and the U.S. declares a public health emergency. February 7th, Chinese medical doctor Li Wenliang dies of the coronavirus after trying to warn people of COVID-19 back in December 2019. Dr. Wenliang was visited by Chinese police and forced to sign a statement denouncing his warning as an unfounded and illegal rumor.

**March 2020.** COVID-19 gains pandemic status. President Trump declares a national emergency. The WHO has still not declared COVID-19 a pandemic. The travel ban on non-US citizens traveling from Europe comes into effect. Italy experienced over a thousand deaths a day in March. Virtual health visits, stay-at-home work, and stay-at-home orders become an everyday fact of life.

**April 2020.** New York hospitals are overflowing, and the demand for ventilators overwhelms the healthcare system. The Senate passes the Coronavirus Aid, Relief, and Economic Security (CARES) Act. The young, poor, and elderly avoid care for COVID-19 symptoms for various reasons, mostly out of fear. President Trump starts Operation Warp Speed to create a vaccine for COVID-19 through private enterprises. The WHO finally labels COVID-19 a pandemic. A New York emergency room physician, Dr. Lorna Breen commits suicide because of the COVID-19 crisis. MLB Baseball player, Drew Robinson, attempts suicide. 12-year-old Hayden Hunstable commits suicide four days before his 13th birthday.

**May 2020.** A saliva-based test to detect the COVID-19 infection is made available. An American immunologist and chief medical adviser to the U.S. president, Dr. Fauci testifies that the death toll is likely being underestimated. Vaccines are in full production with phase-3 trials. May is Mental-Health Awareness Month. Zak Williams, son of actor Robin Williams, speaks on the Dr. Oz show to support Mental-Health Awareness and about his father's suicide.

**June 2020.** U.S. COVID cases reach 2 million. A CDC survey found that a quarter of adults aged 18 to 24 had "seriously considered suicide" in the 30 days before completing the survey.

**July 2020.** COVID-19 cases reach 100,000 per day in the U.S. Cancer deaths increased because of delayed care. The vaccines show some effectiveness, congress grants more money to businesses, and an antibody treatment is now available for severe COVID-19 infections. A study from the CDC revealed that 40 percent of Americans reported some mental-health issue or substance abuse related to the pandemic.

**August 2020.** Co-morbidities like obesity and diabetes significantly increase the mortality risk from COVID-19 infections, and Joe Biden calls for a three-month mask mandate, even outdoors. COVID-19 is the third leading cause of death in the U.S. However, overall mortality for the year was about the same, sparking major debates. The FDA clears convalescent plasma to treat COVID-19. Politically motivated groups attack the drug hydroxychloroquine. Dr. Anthony Fauci announced on national television that the drug Remdesivir (costing thousands), should be "standard of care" in the treatment of COVID-19 infections. Studies later revealed that it helped little in preventing death from COVID-19. The politics of fear was obscuring the science of a rapidly spreading virus. A CDC study showed that one-quarter of young adults contemplated suicide during the pandemic.

**September 2020**. The U.S. rejects the WHO global vaccine effort with the COVAX scheme. Most mRNA vaccines are now in phase-3 trials. The CDC pulls a document from its website stating the COVID-19 virus is airborne. Former President Trump is infected with the COVID-19 virus and is discharged from the hospital three days later. It is later revealed that President Trump received experimental treatments, mono-clonal antibodies, and plasma. In Japan, 1,805 people commit suicide.

**October 2020**. Global cases top 40 million, and the U.S. death toll stands at 220,000. A Japanese CNN media outlet reports more Japanese people died of suicide (2,153) in October than during the entire COVID-19 crisis (2,087); with 705 of those being working class men.

**November 2020**. COVID-19 cases eclipse 100,000 per day. Democrat Joe Biden is determined to be the U.S. president-elect. An article in Nature shows indoor, under-ventilated spaces contribute to COVID-19's spread. The WHO changes the longstanding definition of herd immunity as the indirect protection from an infectious disease through vaccination or previous infection: the language of "previous natural infection" is removed, so that the definition only includes immunity related to vaccination. A new outbreak races across Europe and the United States.

**December 2020**. U.S. health care workers and the elderly receive the COVID-19 vaccine. The coronavirus was likely in the U.S. as early as December 2019. COVID-19 cases surge after the Thanksgiving holiday. Deaths rise back up to over 2,000 per day per the CDC website. Depression and suicide decrease during the

Christmas holidays, likely because people use their best coping skills during these times. San Francisco reports a staggering 700 people had died from drug overdose in 2020, far outpacing the 200 COVID-19 deaths. Clark County School District in Las Vegas, Nevada, reports 18 students had committed suicide in 2020; the youngest victim was 7-years-old.

**January 2021.** Joe Biden takes the oath of office as the 46th President of the United States, while former President Trump battles a second impeachment trial after the Capitol protests turn violent. Maryland Representative, Jamie Raskin buries his son, Tommy Raskin, the day before the riots, who had committed suicide on New Year's Eve. Two police officers who were at the capitol riots commit suicide in the weeks following the incident. Rodney Moore, Sr. of California, loses his 14-year-old son to suicide. The California Department of Public Health reports that 134 people under 18 died by suicide in 2020 jumping from the Golden Gate Bridge; a 24 percent increase from 2019.

**February 2021.** President Biden visits a memorial to commemorate the over 500,000 in the U.S who have died from COVID-19. Millions of people are vaccinated in the U.S.; other countries are struggling to receive the vaccines. A Lancet Psychiatry study reports that eight percent of 9- and 10-year-olds reported suicidal thoughts and two percent reported a suicide attempt. India estimates they lose 28 student lives each day to suicide. According to official records in India, the state of Kerala reported 173 children aged 10 to 18-years-old, died by suicide during the lockdown.

**March 2021.** COVID-19 cases begin to come, down and all three major U.S. vaccines (Johnson & Johnson, Moderna, and Pfizer) are in distribution in the U.S. Two Chicago Police officers die by suicide within one week.

**April 2021.** Globally, COVID-19 deaths surpass 3 million. A new study in JAMA Psychiatry concludes in the U.S., the risk of suicide compared with the general population was significantly greater for nurses.

Consider the number of suicides in Japan in September and October (3,958). There were more suicides in those two months than from COVID-19 in the whole year (2,087). What about the 173 student suicides in Kerala,

India; the 18 Clark County School District student deaths in 2020. What about the fact that police suicide increased by nearly 40 percent during the COVID-19 crisis? In some countries, it is undeniable more people are dying from non-COVID deaths than COVID deaths. People rationalize that the most important things are the public-health measures against the only thing that currently seems to matter: COVID-19. All the noise from the media outlets has made us deaf to the fact many people were and still are taking their own lives.

During the COVID-19 crisis, we have instituted unprecedented public health actions to curb the spread of the virus to reduce human contact. While these steps reduce the rate of infections (and conceivably deaths), there are unintended consequences. The COVID-19 public health interventions lead to a variety of economic, psychosocial, and health-related consequences. Economic stress affects everyone, everywhere. The 2008 financial crisis caused thousands of suicides worldwide.

The economic stress resulting from the COVID-19 crisis is grossly underestimated. In 2020, we saw millions of jobs lost or furloughed, medical care delayed, and an overwhelming wave of anxiety, fear, and depression. Many Americans fell into poverty for the first time. Over 54 million Americans filed for unemployment, and 60 million EU jobs were put at risk. Government relief packages could cause a worldwide deficit of 30 trillion dollars by 2030. Closed businesses, canceled public events, furloughs, and shelter-in-place strategies may well lead to a recession. With unemployment, we face isolation, loneliness, hopelessness, and potentially, suicides. The number of suicides in Japan is important to consider from an industry standpoint; many were young working-class men and women, specifically from the travel industry.

Economic downturns are associated with higher suicide rates compared with periods of prosperity. The stock market, unsurprisingly, has experienced historic drops over the last 18 months. However, this extensive economic damage hasn't only been on Wall Street. These lockdowns cause the poor to become poorer, which is often overlooked or denied.

Many parents are forced to take off work because of schools being closed for undetermined periods. Parents worry about their children's disrupted education and their own inability to provide financial stability. Facing such stresses outside of their control, many turn to substance abuse or, even worse, suicide.

Overcrowded emergency rooms are experiencing record high mental-health visits. The mental-health system was originally designed for face-to-face contact but now nearly all mental-health visits are conducted online, which has resulted in unpredictable results. Reduced access to mental-health care negatively affects patients with depression and suicidal ideation. Canceled appointments, virtual visits, and forced at-home-schooling, all create excess stress for mental-health patients.

Strategies that promote social isolation increase the risk of mental illness. Humans require social connections and physical touch. Many rationalize the impacts of social distancing and lockdowns are acceptable as long as we decrease the number of COVID-19 deaths. But the mental-health crisis is increasing exponentially all around us. There is a refusal to believe social isolation can lead to more deaths from suicide and drug overdoses. The tragedies cited in the recent New York Times article in Las Vegas are one such result. Individuals experiencing suicidal ideation often lack social connections and family structure. From a suicide prevention perspective, it is concerning that the most critical public health strategy for the COVID-19 crisis is social and physical distancing, the very strategy that also contributes to mental-health deterioration and suicidal ideation.

Family and friends remain isolated from loved ones who are admitted to hospitals, mental care clinics, and elderly care homes. This is creating barriers to mental-health treatment. Notre Dame economists wrote there is a substantially higher rate of non-COVID deaths among the elderly in nursing homes, especially those suffering from Alzheimer's disease and dementia. When a loved one goes to the emergency room, the family cannot stay and, sometimes, this is the last moment that person might have with their family members. Many COVID-19 patients feel as if they are being sent away to die. Doctors are instructing patients to go home and "rest" and just wait out their COVID-19 infection. Information about alternative therapies, as diet and lifestyle optimization, or other actions patients could take for themselves, are seldom discussed. Most have to search the Internet to find alternative therapies to treat their condition.

## SUICIDE AND COVID-19: A PERFECT STORM?

Has COVID-19 been a perfect storm for suicide in the U.S.? Modeling studies predicted suicide rate increases ranging from 1 to 145 percent. Suicide rates have risen in the U.S. over the last 30 years and peaked in 2018 with 48,344 deaths, the highest since 1942. Preliminary statistics show the U.S. recorded about 44,843 suicide deaths in 2020, which is a 5.6 percent decline compared to 2019 according to a Journal of the American Medical Society (JAMA) study. It is essential to highlight the CDC waited longer than usual to release 2020 suicide statistics; something that has never happened until now.

You might assume with the reports of increased depression, isolation, lack of mental-health resources, higher emergency room psychiatric visits, and the other negative effects from the lockdowns, the suicide rates would have been sky high. In fact, they were not higher in 2020 according to studies. It is important to look at the mental-health crisis as it has always existed to study this question better. As, we said, there's more than COVID-19 killing people and the answer may surprise you.

The rates in Japan also shed light on this question. Japan was one of the few countries to release its suicide data in early 2020. There was in fact no overall increase in the number of suicides in 2020 for Japan. But suicides in young working-class females increased by over 20 percent in August and September 2020. Suicides by women less than 40 years of age experienced an astonishing 63 percent increase in August 2020 compared to the same month in the past three years. The number of suicides among students was also notably higher in August and September of 2020 than the corresponding numbers of past years. The mental-health status among young women suggests adverse economic conditions due to job or income loss.

Japan's highest rate of suicide was in 2003, with 34,000 people killing themselves. That figure had fallen in 2019 with just over 20,000 suicides. Similar trends exist for the U.S. after a crisis. In the immediate aftermath of the first lockdowns in this case, the data indicates a short-term decrease in suicides, attributed to the "honeymoon period" or the "pulling together phenomenon." We saw similar trends after the 1918 influenza, SARS, and Ebola epidemics. Several suicidologists believe that the preliminary numbers for suicide deaths may be grossly underestimated. This may be due to the fact that current data does not separate the COVID-19 deaths from mental-illness deaths. It is simply impossible to know how many of the 500,000 COVID-19 deaths (in the U.S.) would have otherwise died by suicide. This alone obscures the research. Suicide rates among the elderly are among the highest and they make up over 80 percent of COVID-19 deaths. Who knows how many of these would have committed suicide? Drug overdose deaths also confuse the numbers. How many suicides were misclassified as other so-called deaths of despair (drug overdose and alcohol-related deaths). If a first responder finds a dead person without a suicide note or other evidence, then that person would be labeled a drug overdose, regardless of whether it was a suicide or not. The president of the American Association of Suicidology, Dr. Jonathan Singer, is quoted saying he wouldn't be surprised if some deaths that were ruled an overdose were actually suicide deaths. The suicide rate is down for 2020, but it does not take away from the fact that many committed suicide during the lockdowns who might have not otherwise.

In states like Illinois and Maryland, suicide rates among black residents doubled during the lockdowns. The rate of adolescent suicide rose during the lockdowns. Perhaps more indicative, the sheer number of adolescents and adults reporting depression and mental illness is very high. After COVID-19 is past us, the impact of a devastated economy, the lost education of a generation, the failed businesses and love loved-ones will affect people for many years to come. **The COVID-19 crisis impacts suicide, but the salient point is that suicide is, and has always been a major cause of death, even though it is treatable**.

There's more than COVID-19 killing people: the denial of suicides, murders, drug overdoses, and starvation to name a few. The key component of denial is the minimization of depression, suicides, starvation, and drug overdoses associated with the lockdowns. The most common example of denial is malnutrition. According to the United Nations, starvation kills around 25,000 people per day, but we rarely speak about it. Studies have projected globally, we will see 100 million deaths associated with malnutrition and delayed medical care years after the COVID-19 pandemic is behind us. We even have a vaccine for starvation - it is called food; one-hundred percent effective with zero side effects. However, its prominence is neither reflected in our perceptions of death, nor in the media.

The U.S. COVID-19 daily death rate at its peak was on the same level as digestive disorders and diabetes. Suicide is the tenth leading cause of death. Ignoring the danger of the coronavirus is difficult for many as we are still gathering, traveling, and telling ourselves that it will not happen to us. Many have refused the vaccines and to wear masks. This complacence may be due to the fact we naturally fight off thousands of viruses at any given time using our immune systems. However, the COVID-19 virus is ubiquitous and more complex than we as humans.

The obsession with denialism is dangerous, and it needlessly alienates the interested public with false accusations. It also results in a stifled debate about issues that genuinely deserve discussion. The result is that if you do not go along with the narrative, you are an outsider and denialist. The decision to close or open the schools, or what medications to use, results from the narrative. There are good arguments on both sides of the issue but arguing to reopen schools is met with forceful skepticism. The signs of denial are rationalization, justification, minimization, excuse-making, and refusal. It's our human nature to use denial to eliminate the discomfort of accepting realities we'd rather not acknowledge. This is part of cognitive dissonance. Denial is a protective mechanism for emotional survival. Humans use other tools like intuition to protect us from various things. Denial challenges you to ask yourself, "What do I see here?"

Suicide is a major concern, but it is treatable. The former head of the National Institute of Mental Health, Dr. Thomas Insel once explained,

*"Modern medicine has been successful at bending the curve, or decreasing deaths, in almost every disease known to man - cardiovascular disease, cancer, diabetes, malaria, and others. But suicides have never gone down in over thirty years, despite over numerous medications for suicide and depression."*

Suicide occurs worldwide, affecting individuals of all nations, races, cultures, religions, and gender. We define suicide as death caused by self-directed injurious behavior with the intent to die. Suicidal ideation refers to thinking about, considering, or planning on suicide. According to U.S. data, firearms are the most common method of suicide, followed by suffocation and poisoning.

To sum up, there are about one million suicide deaths globally each year. Over one million Americans made plans and attempted suicide in 2019. Surprisingly, the highest suicide rates occur in Lithuania, Guyana, and

South Korea. It is undeniable that the COVID-19 crisis has contributed to many of these suicides. The increase in mental-health issues is the invisible problem of the COVID-19 crisis that nobody is discussing. Suicide is being discussed as the "invisible blood" in the pandemic because they do not count suicides as deaths associated with COVID-19.

Previous Epidemics and Suicide: Learning from History

Past epidemics are helpful to understand the impact of a pandemic on suicide rates. Little compares in our recent lifetime with the magnitude of the COVID-19 crisis. The last comparable crisis was the Spanish flu pandemic in 1918, caused by the H1N1 influenza viruses. About 500 million people or one-third of the world's population became infected with the Spanish flu virus. At least 50 million people perished worldwide, including about 670,000 people in the United States. Many were affected by the death of a loved one. Parents lost children and many children found themselves orphans. The Spanish flu epidemic saw an increase in death by suicide. Norwegian scientist Svenn-Erik Mamelund studied the impact of the Spanish Flu on mental-health. He found it increased the number of first-time psychiatric hospitalizations in Norway as compared to pre-Spanish Flu times. He also documented an increased rate of suicide in the U.S. He blamed a decrease in social integration and interaction during the epidemic and the fears caused by the epidemic, for the increased suicides.

Because the definition of suicide was not established in the 1920 and 1930s, it was difficult to study. The First World War had just ended, and other socio-economic factors such as strict food rationing, prohibition, and the Great Depression, were present. It is also important to highlight the absence of mass communication outlets (television and internet) offset the potential impact of suicides. It acts as an amplifier for the messages carried by newspapers and radio stations. We are experiencing the same fears of social isolation and suicide during the current COVID-19 epidemic.

Source: Mamelund, SE. Effects of the Spanish Influenza Pandemic of 1918-19 on Later Life Mortality of Norwegian Cohorts Born About 1900. 2003.

Prevention is the Cure for COVID-19

Today's global health care challenge is how to tackle the increasing burden of chronic disease that results in premature death and misery for tens of millions of people. History reveals that the most substantial determinant of health and longevity have little to do with hospitals and more about the community. We fight off thousands of viruses every year using our immune systems. Even after COVID-19 is managed, it's likely another pandemic will strike. So, how do arm ourselves with the tools and the resilience to fight a future virus? We must naturally support our immune system so that we are better equipped to fight off infection. Metabolic diseases are the major factor putting many at risk of dying from COVID-19. Obesity and diabetes are common examples of metabolic disease; they are preventable and rapidly reversible. Governments would save millions of lives if they encouraged the message: Eating real food saves lives. Long before COVID-19, diet-related diseases were overstretching many national health systems. Even 20 years ago, the WHO declared obesity a global epidemic, yet, not only have we failed to curb it, it's now far worse than at any time in human history. Obesity and diabetes are only the tip of the iceberg.

The current primary focus for COVID-19 is to devise a vaccine as quickly as possible but based on what we know about influenza. A vaccine is likely to have some limitations in its effectiveness and impact if the population is obese and or metabolically unhealthy.

Source: Malhotra, A. The 21-Day Immunity Plan. 2020. Yellow Kite Books.

# CHAPTER FOUR:
## THE PSYCHOLOGICAL IMPACT OF SUICIDE AND THE COVID-19 CRISIS

*"Fear out of control erodes our perceived wellness."*
—Tom Pyszczynski

When over half of the planet was in some kind of lockdown, we performed the largest psychology experiment ever, and the effects were observed rippling throughout every aspect of human life. Despite what lockdowns are meant to achieve, they create more harm than good. Paradoxically, many of the lockdown measures are associated with numerous health conditions, all contributing to non-COVID deaths. The lockdowns in many countries were having drastic effects on people's physical and mental-health, resulting in excess mortality from sources such as malnutrition, delayed health care, increased infectious disease (measles, polio, malaria, and cholera), missed vaccinations, increased inequalities due to school closures and unemployment, and mental-health issues such as depression and suicide.

Mass lockdowns began in China and seemed prudent because, at first, they appeared to work. Before 2020, no country had ever attempted a mass lockdown. When governments were enthusiastically advocating lockdowns, few considered the consequences. Everyone knew there would be a cost to being complicit in shutting down the economy, isolating ourselves in our homes, and avoiding social and physical contact.

Why did we all go along with the lockdowns? Many feel the media, our governments and health officials manipulated our doubts and fears. Mortality salience is heightened by the constant, sensationalist media coverage of the impending apocalypse. Agnotology and cognitive dissonance help explain why we continued to comply with the lockdowns. Agnotology is the study of culturally-induced ignorance or doubt, particularly dealing with the publication of inaccurate or misleading scientific data. Cognitive dissonance is the state of having inconsistent thoughts, beliefs, or attitudes, especially regarding behavioral decisions and attitude change. This is how we make sense of circumstances that are beyond comprehension. Behaviors are maintained by indirect and subtle forces and these uncertain times germinate poor and conflicting explanations based on emotion. For example, when a situation is presented as a social dilemma (school closures or masks), this increases adherence to lockdown rules, even though these measures are based on weak evidence. The European monitoring of excess mortality for public health action shows that the number of COVID-19 positive cases increased to hundreds of thousands per day during the lockdowns; despite over 80 percent of Americans and Europeans complying with mask mandates since August 2020.

Lockdowns have turned out as badly as the health experts warned, for exactly the reasons they predicted. Several authors have commented on the harms of non-evidence-based measures many countries have taken based on failed predictions of the severity of the problem. We knew the effects of lockdowns before COVID-19. Dr. Robert Redfield, the director of the CDC under former president Trump, warned about the significant mental-health consequences of lockdowns. Dr. Maria Van Kerkhove, of the WHO COVID-19 response team stated, "lockdowns are a blunt, sheer-force instrument with severe social and economic consequences." WHO epidemic response strategies typically involve infection control, the strengthening of health systems, and bolstering of mental-health resources. However, the intense focus on SARS-COVID-2 virus transmission led scientists and government leaders to overlook the psychosocial trauma to individuals and communities.

Governments seem indifferent to the adverse effects of prolonged lockdowns. During the 2002 SARS outbreak, people who were isolated for over 10 days showed significantly higher PTSD. Localized lockdowns caused severe psychological damage, and scientists concluded that the potential benefits of mandatory mass quarantine needed to be weighed carefully against the possible psychological costs.

Flashing forward to 2021 and beyond, there's more than just the psychological costs to consider. We must take stock of the number of non-

COVID patients affected, acknowledging that these will likely be much greater than actual deaths from COVID-19. Pandemic data reveals that many deaths, including 90 percent of those between 25 and 54, were NOT virus related. It became clear as many nations advocated lockdowns, the unintended effects weigh heavily on the mental and general health of the population. If we didn't know, or at the very least believe it, the grim reality is that social isolation caused by lockdowns cripple those in its grasp. The tragic consequences of loneliness affect even the most stoic of humans.

Lockdowns created extremely harmful health conditions and social problems. The Japanese experience with suicide is important, as we explored in the previous chapter. In September and October 2020, there were nearly 4,000 deaths by suicide in Japan; over 25 percent of those were young working-class men and women between the ages of 20 and 59 years old. Similar to Nevada, the total number of suicides has only slightly increased compared to 2019, but the percentage for young students is much higher.

The impact of isolation on mental-health is both complex and complicated. We are assessing (and will be for a while) the severity of the loss of life, breakdown of families, despair, mourning, and isolation. We ignore that lockdowns affect the most vulnerable people in our communities, such as the unemployed, the elderly, and the mentally and physically disabled. The current decrease in access to mental-healthcare results in the deteriorating health of adults and children; especially those with existing mental-health conditions.

Just carrying the diagnosis of a mental disorder can shorten one's lifespan by a third. Similarly, the stress associated with job loss often predicts a shorter life span. Quarantines have been shown to compromise people's immune systems. The very measures aimed at protecting the vulnerable, such as our elderly, ultimately shorten their lives because the psychological or physical stress compromises their immune systems.

A 2020 CDC survey during the lockdowns revealed that one-third of Americans reported anxiety and depression. Additionally, 20 percent of the survey population thought about death and dying and 25 percent of young adults openly thought about suicide. It is obvious mental-health conditions such as depression and suicide have increased in high proportions. In a study of over 5,000 people in the U.S. and Australia, more than a quarter of those 18 to 24-years old and nearly a third of caregivers (most unpaid) for adults seriously contemplated suicide. The psychological impact of the COVID-19 pandemic on the general population of countries like Saudi Arabia, China, and Spain all show moderate levels of depressive symptoms, anxiety, and general stress. On the other hand, Iran seems to have higher levels of stress than other Middle Eastern countries.

COVID-19 is adding fuel to the already existing mental-health crisis. In Maryland, a JAMA study showed that black men and women were disproportionately impacted by COVID-19, with an increased rate of suicide during the lockdowns. Women are vulnerable to suicide, with increased anxiety about losing their jobs and affecting their children's health and well-being. The pandemic has compounded an existing crisis with high unemployment rates, social isolation, hopelessness, all of which are known risk factors for substance abuse and suicide. The number of crisis hotlines has increased. The lockdowns have decreased support for treatment providers, health departments, and other services that help people with substance abuse disorders.

When compared with 2019, occurrences of anxiety disorders nearly tripled, and suicidal ideation nearly doubled. Mental-health related Emergency Room visits were up 24 percent among children ages 5 to 11. Abrupt disruptions to daily life are a cause for the increase in mental-health problems. At least half of all adults in the United States report their mental-health has been negatively impacted due to worry and stress over the coronavirus. A Chinese study found an increase in anxiety, depression, alcohol abuse, and decreased mental well-being.

More first responders (police officers and firefighters) die from suicide than in the line of duty. These suicides rarely draw media attention. Front-line healthcare professionals taking care of COVID-19 patients have a much higher risk of having depression, anxiety, insomnia, and distress.

Anxiety disrupts the possibility for the best outcome. Previous experience with pandemics has shown that communities respond the best to adverse events when the normal social functioning is least disrupted.

The COVID-19 crisis may not be the best time to learn to overcome our fears and anxieties, though it is surely an opportunity to learn to control them better. During the COVID-19 crisis, it is quite rare to hear about suicides, even though one happens every 40 seconds. The public should be informed about the complexity of suicidal behavior, in which biological, psychological, social, and environmental factors are at play. Everyone needs to be aware and knowledgeable about suicide in order to effectively help someone suffering from suicidal ideation. But despite the tragedies, the disturbing statistics, and heart-breaking stories that have collectively gripped the world, we can draw from the lessons the virus has taught us and look to a brighter future.

Whether or not lockdowns are effective at reducing the spread of the coronavirus is a contentious issue. Quarantine and lockdown are interchangeable terms. Historically, quarantine is derived from Italian "quaranta giornis," meaning 40 days. The term appeared in other pandemics like the Black Plague. They required ships arriving in Venice to remain anchored for 40 days with all crew on board before landing, whether or not anyone was sick. Lockdowns are a "mass quarantine" involving countries, states, cities, villages, and homes. For example, small villages were isolated during the Ebola crisis. Lockdowns include voluntarily social distancing and remaining at home; but sometimes this is mandatory. And this forced isolation is firmly correlated with death, especially with the elderly.

Depriving people of their liberties and normal social interactions in the name of preventing infection and death is contentious. Mass lockdowns are powerfully disruptive to society, as governors and lawmakers continue to believe erroneously that the harder the lockdown, the better the result. Recent experience has revealed this to not be the case. The U.K., France, and Italy enforced some of the strictest lockdowns, requiring police-state tactics. These measures did not stop the spread of the virus. Multiple papers about this have been published. Dozens of countries bypassed individual rights and democratic freedoms, instituting lockdowns in an act of state control unlike anything in the West since the Second World War.

The goals of a lockdown are to reduce the transmission of the virus and rapid increase of illness, or to "flatten the curve." No two countries instituted the same lockdowns, COVID-19 infections increased, and deaths were high despite best efforts. The work of Dr. John Ioannidis supports this, and there are dozens of other papers on the subject listed in the bibliography. Even the strictest of lockdowns cannot prevent viruses that are more complex than we are. A 1969 case report in *The Journal of Hygiene* illustrates this point,

"*There is little doubt that an outbreak of respiratory disease occurred at an*

*Antarctic base after 17 weeks of complete isolation. Six of the twelve men, all devoid of human contact for 4 months, caught the common cold during winter."*

Lockdowns and school closures should not have happened per WHO policies. As previously mentioned, both the CDC and WHO found little evidence to recommend them. The WHO also admits there is little evidence that ordinary masks reduce viral transmission; only that there is a mechanistic plausibility for their potential effectiveness. What went unnoticed is while the media outlets and governors pushed for lockdowns, organizations like the WHO and the CDC rejected these measures as a potential solution to the epidemic. They only discussed lockdowns and school closings as a *temporary* measure during "severe, very severe, extreme pandemics," like the Spanish flu that killed over 50 million people. They acknowledge the inferior quality of evidence that school closures affect the transmission of viruses such as influenza.

To date, the doomsday predictions have proven to be inaccurate. People often feel the need to explain large events with proportionally large causes. An editor at *The Daily Beast* wrote on Twitter that "Seven percent of all Americans (23 million people) would die." British physicist, David Deutsch might suggest these are ideas based on "poor explanations." Compare that to the U.K. Prime Minister Boris Johnson, who was quoted as saying that vaccinations have not really been effective: "It's the lockdowns that made the difference."

A skillfully crafted narrative can convince men to give away all their worldly goods or to happily send their wives to the storyteller's bed. We are programmed to fall prey to cognitive dissonance and confirmation bias, clinging to those facts most consistent with our beliefs. The more people who share the same misconception, the more likely we are to believe it. It is not until the crisis, and tragedy, touches us personally that we come to terms with the delusion. If an incorrect belief becomes prevalent enough, it acquires a critical mass. Though unrelated to the pandemic, a stark reminder of this is when over 900 people (304 of them children) simultaneously committed suicide under the direction of Jim Jones in Africa. We often mold the facts to fit our pre-existing opinions. We intentionally ignore those facts that do not confirm our beliefs. We hold onto our beliefs up to the point that disconfirming information can no longer be ignored.

Many media outlets have opted to present information in a biased manner, possibly to create a uniform narrative. Doing so helps people to follow guidelines issued by governments and health organizations. Since the pandemic's beginning, the news media seems to have followed a narrative with forecasts of doom via media-fed misrepresentations. In a pandemic, it seems nearly impossible for the news media to deliver a balanced message. Corporate propaganda, heavy media reporting, and endless television ads aimed to convince the public that lockdowns were for the best. Even worse, media outlets like CNN and the New York Times fully supported the lockdowns and treated mass protests as fringe events related to politic dissent. The state governors who initiated the most severe lock downs saw the biggest jumps in television approval ratings. This governmental "fear mongering" has been clear with COVID-19. Fear is psychological and currently it is pathological.

Once the pandemic became politicized, most media outlets seemed to have done their best to mislead people about who is to blame for the problems of the pandemics. You can verify this by asking yourself how many times you have heard the phrase, "Are you and your family at risk?" regarding the latest infection. The decline of objectivity in journalism is evident. Simply read the same article in the New York Times and the Wall Street Journal. A pertinent example is the media outlets that seldom focus on the fact that the median age of death is around 80 years old. Even when the articles published are blatantly inaccurate, the media outlets seldom rectify or redact their stories.

The media have "fear-locked" people with the coverage of the COVID-19 events. Journalists have failed. A news reporter's job is to question authority and be sure people hear the truth and the facts. The news media often portrays a pre-arranged narrative. A relevant example is murder rates. Between 1990 and 1998, the U.S. murder rate decreased by twenty percent, while murder stories on media newscasts increased by an astonishing 600 percent. The news does not give a complete coverage of any topic; rather, they post stories in the narrative that fits their agenda, whether political, monetary, or both. Most people do not read the newspaper critically enough to intelligently decide whether the subject is true or marked by bias. This type of narrow and polarizing media coverage increases depression, anxiety, and substance abuse, leading to increased suicidal behaviors, which was evident during the financial crisis.

Media coverage influences and promotes suicidal behaviors. Round the clock media coverage infuses into our sleep and raises anxiety and suicidal behaviors, not to mention the adverse health effects of losing sleep. This was observed in the early 20th century with the Spanish Flu pandemic and The Great Depression. Though arguably and inadvertently responsible for this spike in anxiety in their audiences, media outlets briefly mention suicide rates among children or adults during the lockdowns. News reports of crowded emergency rooms and intensive care units increase public apprehension about seeking help for health issues. Multiple cases of COVID-19 related suicides in the U.S., U.K., Italy, Germany, Bangladesh, India, Israel, and many other countries are reported in the mass media and psychiatric literature. Once fear is turned on, it can lead to overreactions in all directions. For example, in England, a 19-year-old server died in a hospital after a suicide attempt because of the "mental-health impacts" of isolation. In New York City, a 66-year-old man with throat cancer hung himself after testing positive. In Illinois, a man killed his girlfriend and then himself for fear of contracting the COVID-19. They both tested negative for the coronavirus. In Israel, a forced, unexpected lockdown caused a man to take his life in protest at the hotel where everyone was being quarantined. A false choice is one a person makes, which leads to a tragic outcome.

Many deaths are treated as COVID-19 deaths, no matter their actual cause. Social media has become the arbiter of allowable discussion and has censored any subject they feel does not follow a specific narrative. The origin of the virus is one such example. Censorship ensures commitment to the lockdown measures by putting weight on the facts differently, as well as being inattentive to the severe side effects. Politics and universities have tainted science and suppressed the free exchange of ideas that are necessary to uncover scientific truths. Journalists speak little about mental-health problems, while organizations like UNICEF suggest that this will eventually become a global catastrophe.

The COVID-19 crisis has exposed critical fractures in our educational fabric. The educational system is central to addressing the mental-health crisis. We must be forward thinking about our investment in education. We are undervaluing education by not returning our teachers and students back to school. Perhaps we will eventually observe a paradigm shift in the educational model because of the COVID-19 crisis. Even prior to the pandemic, an inequitable distribution of resources existed in our education system. We need a life beyond virtual learning to avoid toxic coping strategies. Families who depend on schools for de facto childcare are forced to choose between going without food, rent, and a healthy learning environment. Parents in these circumstances feel helpless and shameful for not being able to provide financial stability and education. These choice-less "choices" foster a malignant environment of competition.

Our current situation is an opportunity to change the system and give our students and teachers greater attention. People talk about a "return to normal." Hopefully, we use the pandemic as a learning experience to make vital changes and improve. We will need mental-health professionals, nurses, and counselors in every school to handle the oncoming mental-health crisis resulting from lockdowns.

## DRUG OVERDOSES

The national data is still incomplete, but information suggests that U.S. drug overdoses are on track to reach an all-time high. Addiction experts blame the pandemic, leaving people isolated and disrupting treatment and vital recovery programs.

"Overdoses are surging." New York, Seattle, San Francisco, Las Vegas, and other cities are reporting an increase in overdose deaths. Daniel Buccino, the clinical manager of the John Hopkins Broadway center for addiction, says, "We are seeing more of those cases going straight to the morgue rather than to the emergency department." Nearly 100,000 people died from drug overdoses in 2020. Over 70 percent were from the opioid drug fentanyl. In San Francisco, overdose deaths increased 173 percent between 2018 and 2020. More than 800 people died of drug overdoses in San Francisco in 2020, compared to 254 deaths from COVID-19. Opioid overdose deaths would be far worse if not for the 4,300 times the opioid reversal drug, Narcan (naltrexone), was administered in 2020. The Narcan data from the Drug Overdose Prevention project is self-reported and is probably a major undercount.

The opioid crisis is intensifying because of the rapid increase in fentanyl use compared to that of morphine. Fentanyl is about 50 times more potent than morphine. The respiratory system stops functioning after taking fentanyl, and people stop breathing. In April of 2020, police officer Derek Chauvin, knelt on African American George Floyd's neck while apprehending him, which inadvertently led to Floyd's death. This catapulted the Black Lives Matter (BLM) movement back into the media's spotlight. The defense lawyers in the George Floyd case argued that he had three times the lethal dose of fentanyl in his system when he was killed by Derek Chauvin. Most of the overdoses have occurred in low-income apartment buildings and city-funded homeless shelters. Many others have died on sidewalks and in parks.

In the 1800s, Great Britain flooded China with opium, derailing its economy and population. Today, China is behind the fentanyl crisis, with the Mexican cartels all too happy to help facilitate its distribution into the U.S. The overdose problem is a public health crisis costing thousands of lives.

Lockdown policies had a devastating indirect effect on drug overdoses. People react to prolonged isolation and stress with dysfunctional coping strategies, resulting in substance abuse and deaths from overdose. Relapse rates for substance abuse disorders range between 40 and 80 percent with standard treatment. Lockdowns reduce contact between people by as much as 75 percent. Isolation is the worst thing for drug addicts; it exposes them to a high risk of death from overdose. The Rat Park theory of drug dependency is very relevant. Dr. Alexander showed that animals would not choose the drugged water when they are happy and bonded in their environment. However, when they are isolated, they resort to the drugged water and overdose a hundred percent of the time. A 48-year-old West Virginian man, just being alone for five days, became anxious and depressed. He relapsed into taking his opioid pain killer. His original addiction followed a shoulder surgery, which he overcame. He blames the isolation and loneliness from the lockdown for his relapse. Once he was called back to work, he stopped using it.

On the "business" side of illegal drugs, according to the Drug Enforcement Agency, the pandemic has also disrupted the supply of drugs from Mexico which can heighten risks for users who seek new dealers and buy unfamiliar products. These unforeseen and dangerous consequences resulted in a rash of overdoses and deaths. People with a history of substance abuse experience higher levels of psychological stress, and these behaviors may persist for years after a pandemic has ended. Coupled with the decrease in mental-health services, there are fewer qualified people to help.

The opioid crisis is still developing. Some emergency rooms are experiencing a 1,000 percent increase in overdose cases. Even worse, the subject of overdoses is not adequately covered by the media. These problems are not exclusive to adults. Children are deeply affected by drug overdoses. A study from the journal, *Pediatrics*, showed that drug overdoses during the pandemic have risen in children. The CDC and scientific journals have reported that over 40 states in the U.S. have reported increases in opioid related deaths since the pandemic's beginning. In Kentucky, early 2020 saw almost as many overdose deaths as had been seen in all of 2019. In Minnesota, the drug overdose rate for African Americans was nearly twice that of other ethnicities.

Iceland and Sweden score very high in every ranking of quality of life and social equity, yet the number of drug-related deaths in these countries is rising. The National Institute for Health and Welfare has shown that overdose deaths by fentanyl are up in Iceland; overdose deaths by heroin are up in Sweden; and overdose deaths from the drug buprenorphine have increased in Finland.

If we want to know the actual effects of the lockdowns, look no further than the vastly increased number of deaths from overdoses. The COVID-19 and the opioid crisis have collided, and the unfortunate statistics show the global impact. In 2017, about 585,000 people died worldwide because of drugs, with opiate narcotics accounting for the majority of deaths. In the U.S., about 70,000 people die annually from opioid overdoses. The 2020 statistics for drug-related deaths are not yet available, but they are projected to be much higher than average. Twenty million people in the United States have a substance abuse disorder. This could be partly attributed to factors such as the economic downturn and unemployment in a year in which over 50 million Americans lost their jobs. The lockdowns during the COVID-19 crisis have left many people with uncertainty, insecurity, and feelings of hopelessness. Even prior to the coronavirus, opioid overdose was the leading cause of accidental deaths in the U.S.; 2020 has only made things worse.

# CHAPTER FIVE:
## SUICIDE AND DEPRESSION IN ADOLESCENTS, VETERANS, AND FIRST RESPONDERS

*"The Pandemic may have been a perfect storm,*
*but we've all been in very different boats."*
—Paul Nestadt M.D.
Johns Hopkins University Psychiatrist

## ADOLESCENTS AND DEPRESSION AND SUICIDE

*"I want to kill myself,"* announced the Jefferson Elementary School students to their counselor, Olivia Carter: some as young as 8 years-old, in Cape Girardeau, Missouri. Carter started working there in 2016 and seldom remembers using the school suicide protocol. Nowadays, it's one a month. She often answers questions like, "What happens when you die?" She feels a good number of the kids understand what it means to end their life by suicide.

The impact of lockdowns on children reaches far beyond anything we could have imagined. UNICEF warns that 1.2 million children could die from malaria, pneumonia, and diarrhea during the lockdowns in developing countries. The key findings of a survey in Asia revealed an increase in human trafficking for sexual exploitation; a surge in child labor and child marriage; an increase in school dropouts; a drastic reduction in household income and savings; food and ration shortages during the lockdowns; increased mental-health problems such as trauma, anxiety, depression, and despair; an increase in child suicide, especially in poor communities.

Dr. Robert Redfield highlighted that over seven million kids get their mental-health services at schools and that the U.S. is seeing an increase in drug use and suicide in adolescent individuals. The curtailing of in-person counseling has had negative effects on treating youth with mental-health disorders. These children are at high risk of further mental-health problems as well as depression. A survey by Young Minds revealed that 80 percent of young people with mental illness reported worsening of their condition because of lockdown measures. With the exceptionally low risk of COVID-19 in younger people, the risk is not worth the reward. Child and adolescent suicide resulting from the lockdowns are catastrophic and complex. It seems like the perfect array of factors coming together, precipitating a child to want to take his or her own life.

The COVID-19 crisis has taken a heavier emotional and psychological toll on young people than adults. Firmly linking adolescent suicides to lockdowns and school closings is complicated, but mental-health emergencies and youth suicide rates have increased to alarming levels. The Children's Hospital Association reported the number of children ages 6 to 12 who visited children's hospitals for suicidal thoughts or self-harm had more than doubled between 2016 (2,555) and 2019 (5,485). Statistics are not yet available for 2020. Visits for teenagers with suicidal thoughts also rose 44 percent in the same period. A recent *Lancet Psychiatry* study highlighted that eight percent of children ages 9 - 10, reported suicidal thoughts and two percent initiated an actual suicide attempt. Rates of youth suicidal ideation have drastically increased in pediatric emergency departments during the 2020 COVID-19 crisis. A CDC study showed that emergency departments are treating more children per day for mental-health conditions. At the Riley Hospital for Children in Indianapolis, the number of children and teens hospitalized after suicide attempts went up from 67 in 2019, to 108 in 2020. Children's Hospital of Oakland reported a 66 percent increase in 10- to 17-year-olds screening positive for suicidal ideation in the emergency department. Intermountain Mental Health Services have reported a 25 percent increase in mental-health referrals since COVID-19. One spokesperson for the Muir Medical Center in Walnut Creek, California reported that they've seen "a year's worth of suicide attempts in just 4 weeks." While children and youth are no more sick with the SARS-CoV-2 (COVID-19) than they would be during an average flu season, this data reflects the highest proportion of suicidal adolescents ever recorded.

Adolescent suicides are typically impulsive and unpredictable. The COVID-19 crisis has created conditions unlike anything mental-health professionals have ever encountered. Suicidal thoughts and self-harm have been well documented in teenagers, but less attention has been paid to young children, despite the growing crisis of adolescent suicide. Youths with no history of mental-health disorders are suddenly contemplating suicide. One reason might be that over 37,000 children have lost a parent to COVID-19. The President of the American Association of Suicidology, Jonathan Singer, says, "It's probably going to be worse for those who were already struggling or disadvantaged by society. Little kids essentially lost a year of socialization." Lockdowns aggravate underlying problems such as parental pressure, parental scolding, household discord, domestic violence, substance abuse, firearms, and inability to escape abusive environments.

Is COVID-19 to blame for all this? Certainly, the COVID-19 crisis adds fuel to the fire, but many counselors and teachers point to the increase in cell phones and social media at young ages. Many elementary school children already have cell phones. More kids are staying up late checking their phones and social media, resulting in poor sleep. Financial factors may be especially prevalent among minority ethnic groups. A 2016 study found that children aged 5 to 11 who died by suicide were more likely to be African Americans and males. Similar findings exist for other minority groups. This begs the question, "Where are the tell-tale signs for these troubled youth?" Depression and self-harm do not look the same in young children as they do in teens and adults. Children are more likely to draw pictures or tell a friend about their suicidal thoughts. They may also appear less interested in playing outside or with others.

Nurse and single mom, Brandi Bielicki, experienced how deadly a mental-health crisis can be for a child. Ms. Bielicki saw no signs her daughter felt suicidal. Kodie was an easygoing child and very close to her mom. She left no clues in her diary nor text messages at school or home. Bielicki recalls. "One day, Kodie called me to say that she lost a tooth." When Brandi returned home, her daughter's door was open, and the authorities later found her body in a nearby field with a short note. Kodie had taken a lethal amount of medication. Brandi believes her daughter did something "super-impulsive" and a 10-year-old cannot see past the tip of their nose; therefore, they do not understand the permanence of their actions nor do they even know help is available. Utah passed a law this year requiring elementary schools to offer suicide-preventions programs. Programs like this are badly needed because many schools only have one counselor for roughly every 250 students.

Most parents are astounded to discover when they learn their child is contemplating suicide or self-harm. One study found that parents and caregivers were unaware their children had tried to kill themselves in 88 percent of cases. The reasons children give for self-harming range from being grounded to grieving the loss of a parent. Nowadays, software like GoGuardian is installed on school-issued devices, and monitors search for suicidal or mental-health behaviors.

Rodney Moore Sr. of Anaheim, California, lost his 14-year-old son, Rodney Jr. Moore to suicide in January 2021. Mr. Moore believes his son despaired when his school did not reopen. He explains, *"Rodney Jr's grades started dropping with distance learning. His world changed."* Rodney Jr was an active teenager who adored animals and playing his saxophone. Adriana Moore, Rodney's mother, noted he kept on saying, *"I don't see the point. Nothing's going to get better."* Rodney's parents felt their son was deeply affected and depressed, but they never suspected that it was to such a degree he would take his own life. Mrs. Moore exclaims, "You should never have to say goodbye to your kids. Every time we close our eyes, we see how we found him." Rodney Moore Sr. adds, *"Although the coronavirus didn't take my son's life directly, it took it indirectly."*

There have been multiple suicides of children 12 years and older and shockingly, even as young as seven. Most school districts decided not to reopen in 2020, despite parents' protests. A Baltimore family says the school shutdowns are having a devastating impact on children after their 14-year-old son, Michael Myronuk, took his own life. They blame the isolation and depression secondary to the impacts of the lockdowns. In December, an 11-year-old boy in Woodbridge, California killed himself with a firearm during a Zoom class. In Arizona, the Pima school district in Tucson reported two student suicides this year, while the Vail district reported three. A Maine teenager took his life in December 2020, his father attributing his son's suicide to the isolation of the lockdown.

These continued school closures lead to thousands of people losing their jobs, especially those who provide custodial duties and bus drivers, because shuttered school buildings have no need for them. Children are witnessing parents or relatives succumb to COVID-19, and little effort is being made to deal with the trauma and stress of losing a family member. The fear and insecurities children face stem from the new realities of parents working from home, being home-schooled, and lack of social interaction, often in cramped accommodations. While children attend online classes, they spend inordinate amounts of time in front of the television or computer. Some children fall behind in online classes because they have little access to computers and internet at home. Isolation caused by the lockdowns has resulted in children being overly sensitive to minor domestic issues.

## THE LAS VEGAS YOUTH SUICIDE CRISIS

The lockdowns have been tragic for Las Vegas students. On November 11, 2020, Nevada Governor, Steve Sisolak, opened his virtual town hall meeting with the announcement that another Clark County School District (CCSD) child, this one nine years-old, had committed suicide the prior evening. The cause of death was likely asphyxiation or by a firearm. This was the fourth child suicide in a six-week period. The CCSD has experienced a cluster of student suicides over the 2020 school year, with a total of 18. All suicides occurred between March 16 and December 31. There was only one student suicide in the CCSD in 2019. CCSD superintendent, Jesus Jara argued for reopening schools, claiming isolation during the lockdowns was to blame for the mental-health crisis and student suicides. One student left a note saying he had nothing to look forward to anymore. Clark County, Nevada, has one of the highest youth suicide rates in the nation. The numbers from 2020 are still being tallied. Since Las Vegas schools shut down in March of 2020, an online early warning system called GoGuardian which monitors student's mental-health episodes, has sent over 3,000 alerts to CCSD officials, raising alarms about suicidal thoughts and self-harm.

A Las Vegas counselor at Shadow Ridge High School recounted the story of one of her students, whom she had known since he was a freshman. This student had overcome much during the 2019-2020 school year. He was living homeless in a park, and the school even accommodated his schedule so he could work at McDonald's. Two weeks before graduation, the counselor sent him an email saying how proud she was of his accomplishments, only to learn that he had recently killed himself with a firearm. Another Las Vegas boy lost two family members during the crisis; one of them from the coronavirus. His father had lost his small business and his mother was working 70 hours a week. The boy recalled how he felt like he no longer had control over his world and that he was a burden. His mother received a call from the school's principal, alerting her that her son was contemplating suicide. She was able to avert the suicide attempt.

On November 9, 2020, the grandfather of a 12-year-old boy with no prior history of mental problems received a call from the CCSD alerting him the boy was possibly going to commit suicide. At 10 p.m., his father found him in his room with a noose around his neck he had constructed with multiple shoestrings. The boy searched the internet on "how to make a noose" using a school-issued iPad. The CCSD monitoring program, GoGuardian, detected the boy's search activity and alerted the school who called the boy's grandfather. His father rushed to his room and aborted the suicide attempt. His parents asked, "Why?" The only things the boy said were that "*I miss my friends*" and "*I don't have friends.*" The boy's dog died during the pandemic, but he was otherwise doing well in virtual school. The grandfather said that his grandson was "*Zoomed out,*" and believes the lockdown caused the suicide attempt and that being in the classroom even a few days a week might have helped him. He says his grandson has a hard time functioning in isolation in lockdown. Today, he is doing better, going to counseling and looking to family and friends for support. In the CCSD, 68 schools now use the pilot program GoGuardian, which has led to over 30 interventions where students were considering suicide. This has been especially true in minority and at-risk schools. We must keep in mind that kids have separate lives in school that are important to them.

On April 17, 2020, 12-year-old Hayden Hunstable took his own life just four days before his thirteenth birthday. His father, Brad Hunstable, made a video two days after he buried his son in their hometown of Aledo, Texas. With over 100 million views, the video has garnered considerable attention and exposed the adolescent suicide crisis during the lockdowns. Hayden enjoyed playing football and hanging out with his friends. Before his death, he became consumed by the video game *Fortnite*. His father believes the lockdowns are to blame for his son's death. The Hunstable's created a foundation in their son's name as a public-service-announcement campaign aimed at educating kids and parents on responsible gaming and parental oversight. The foundation's goal is to pass legislation federally mandating resilience classes as core curriculum for K through 12 schools (www.haydenscorner.org).

Las Vegas Family Therapist, Dr. Sheldon Jacobs, author of the book *48: An Experimental Memoir on Homelessness*, works with CCSD students; he believes the current suicide crisis results from the COVID-19 pandemic leading to increases in isolation, anxiety, depression, and PTSD. He bases his beliefs on his contact with the students and parents in the community. The kids he works with are struggling from a lack of social interaction with peers. With many athletic facilities closed, outlets such as sports are no longer available, and the kids find themselves at home eating more and gaining weight. *"The kids are constantly at home, straining their relationships with parents and siblings. Also, kids are developing mental-health concerns based on the unknown and uncertainty of their parents having job loss,"* says Dr. Jacobs.

Another major problem is youth suicides are rarely investigated. In Nevada, the Child Death Review Board is charged with conducting comprehensive reviews of child death cases, including suicides; but a root-cause analysis is performed only if the child had a history with Child Protective Services. In 2020, only one child who committed suicide met these criteria; thus, most youth suicides will never be reviewed by the board. He also mentions it's clear the suicide crisis has hit African Americans a lot harder than it has whites in many states. He quotes a study published in *JAMA Psychiatry* that analyzed the records from 1,079 Maryland residents who died from suicide during the peak of the lockdowns and found African American suicides doubled compared to previous years. Most of the suicides have been from minorities of lower socioeconomic status, which he says is following the national trend. Dr. Jacobs explained people in minority groups face unique economic challenges and losing a job or a loved one might be felt even more intensely by these communities.

Veteran Las Vegas school teacher, Louie Amelburu has been teaching for over 30 years in a high-risk school. He feels the schools were primarily closed in response to COVID-19 fears among teachers, parents, and the school administrations. Mr. Amelburu teaches health education and suicide prevention. Youth suicide has always been a problem in Las Vegas, ever since he can remember. *"It's like the same thing happens every year, and it never changes,"* he claims, while agreeing the lockdowns are fueling the isolation and depression of kids. Mr. Amelburu points out that kids are constantly on their phones looking for recognition and attention. He says that when kids do not get the love and attention they need at home, they will try to find it somewhere else. Enter social media. Amelburu highlights that the internet has provided a way for kids to get how-to descriptions for suicide and lethal means to kill themselves and sometimes others.

He notes, the kids he teaches are very impulsive and many have attention problems. He teaches adherence to structure because that provides comfort for his students. He believes that insomnia and stress are leading to impulsivity and fear. The part of the brain responsible for impulse control is the pecan-shaped amygdala. The amygdala serves as the central processor for fear, stores short-term information, and is involved in impulse control. In fact, many medications designed to treat attention deficit disorder (ADD) stimulate the amygdala. Research shows that kids who are sleep deprived, even for a short period of time, cannot send messages through the amygdala, leading to impulsivity and learning difficulties. We store fear-learning and fear-memories in the prefrontal cortex, which communicates directly with the amygdala. Mr. Amelburu describes the rhetoric on social media such as Twitter and Facebook as *"processed words."* Just like *"processed food"* is bad for us, he also believes that "processed words" - are equally bad and contribute to stress, especially during a lockdown. Finally, Mr. Amelburu sees many kids who have not only reduced daily physical activity but also substantial weight gain. We all know a physically active lifestyle counteracts the mental-health consequences of lockdowns. *"Suicide is preventable. Teachers, parents, and school counselors must stand at the ready to screen for student suicide risk and be ready to provide immediate support,"* he says.

Dana Gentry, a Las Vegas native who writes for the *Nevada Current*, published an article about the youth suicide crisis in Las Vegas. She wrote the youth suicides were not because of the pandemic but rather that this was a normal year for youth suicides and highlighting that Nevada's children are killing themselves at a rate higher than youth in any other state in the nation. She discussed her viewpoints in an interview with the author. Gentry says, *"It's true, that before COVID-19, suicide took the lives of more 12-to 19-year-*

*olds in Nevada than any other cause of death.*" In 2019, 41 youths in Nevada died by suicide compared to 43 in 2020. When Ms. Gentry was questioned about the cluster of recent student suicides in the CCSD. She said she had no explanation, but she did not feel it was because of the pandemic; but rather the mental-health care system, labor market, and justice system exposed by the stress of the pandemic. Suicide is complex, involving layers of risk factors. It is challenging to know the exact factors involved in the deaths of these students, but she may be correct.

Kerala, a small city in India, initially won worldwide praise for the way it had handled the COVID-19 situation. However, as the virus continued to spread its tentacles, Kerala's success with the pandemic was shown to be short-lived, because what resulted was even more alarming: children taking their lives. According to official records, 173 children ages 10 to 18, died by suicide during the lockdown in Kerala. The reasons for the suicides seemed minor: for instance, routine disciplining by parents for skipping online classes or from playing games on smartphones. The isolation caused by the lockdown has also resulted in children being overly sensitive to minor domestic issues. While children attend online classes, they spend the rest of their time in front of the TV and Internet. This has led to psychosocial problems like addiction, lower self-esteem, and decreased interest in physical activities.

The media has disguised the reality that anybody who is not elderly or suffering chronic underlying diseases has a minor risk of dying from COVID-19. Most journalists refuse to assess and report on the data and have distorted the issue, which has led to closing schools. For example, the New York Times ran a prominent story about a handful of pediatric COVID-19 cases appearing to be an intense inflammatory syndrome named Kawasaki's disease. This disease causes widespread inflammation and primarily affects the heart. Kawasaki's disease can also happen with influenza. The media hype around this story resulted in a frenzy, and officials used the story to reason why students should not return to school for the potential fear of catching COVID-19 and Kawasaki's disease. The story of COVID-19 causing Kawasaki's disease was limited to a handful of cases. Even the doctors who at first seemed alarmed retracted their opinions and felt the story was exaggerated. The U.K. Kawasaki Disease Foundation itself discounted these sensational articles. Nevertheless, headlines such as "Deadly illness in children linked to COVID-19" were published when many governors were attempting to reopen schools. The *New York Times* never corrected their story or acknowledged their journalistic faults. Instead, they moved to the next major news topic while, our schools remained closed.

A more recent example, the CDC released a 2021 report that adolescent hospitalizations due to COVID-19 were increasing. Again, the media highlighted the dangers of COVID-19 infections and adolescents, which had been very low since the start of the crisis. What the media failed to report in this instance was over 20 percent of those hospitalizations were for psychiatric emergencies, not COVID-19 infections. News reporting agencies have followed a potentially dangerous narrative, especially in people with mental-health conditions.

Former CDC director, Dr. Robert Redfield, warned that a rise in adolescent suicides would be one of the most substantial public-health consequences of school closings. His predictions were accurate. Early in the pandemic, the Trump administration attempted to reopen schools. The Biden administration has advocated more lockdowns, wearing masks, and even more school closures until the vaccine can be sufficiently distributed. Even Dr. Anthony Fauci, who has pushed for harsh economic restrictions, suggests keeping schools open because of the profound, unintended consequences caused by school closures. With the infinitesimal risk of COVID-19 infection in younger people, the risk of keeping kids out of school does not seem worth the reward. Superintendents across the nation are weighing the benefits of in-person education against the health of the teachers and the educational cost to the students. The risk of student suicides is causing concern in schools in Arizona and Nevada.

When schools reopened in New York City, over 70,000 students and teachers were tested and only 110 were positive. Florida's schools reopened, and most kids returned to the classroom; to date, there have been no "super-spreader" events. Florida was one of the earliest to resume in-person instruction in August 2020 and has had lower COVID-19 infection rates than most other states. Studies from France, Germany, and Sweden reopened schools without a corresponding increase in cases. However, states like California have the lowest rates of children returning to in-person learning. Fear and internal politics have dominated causing, many schools to remain closed.

So is COVID-19 to blame for the increases in youth suicide, or as with health care, housing, the justice system, and the job market, has the COVID-19 crisis exposed longstanding shortcomings, in this case with mental-health provision? COVID-19 has many untoward effects for children. It raises anxiety because of increased screen time, social media usage, not being in school, and a lack of human interaction. The lockdowns have kept kids at home, where they become bored and resort to playing video games and staying up late. Even worse, the kids living at home are at increased danger from those parents who do not secure their firearms or alcohol. According to Nielsen, a marketing research firm, U.S. sales of alcoholic beverages rose 55 percent in the week ending March 21, 2020, compared with 2019; online alcohol sales also jumped 243 percent. Firearms have increased suicide adolescent deaths, both accidental and suicidal, during the pandemic. During the first 6 months of the pandemic, there was a surge in fatal and non-fatal gun injuries in young children.

Children are undoubtedly aware of the effects COVID-19 is having - they can see the economic impacts on the family. Children learn by example. When they see their parents stressed out, they are likely to follow. Barricading children from the realities of the COVID-19 crisis is not helpful; it's likely harmful. Parents need to play a more proactive role in their children's well-being. Adults are better prepared to deal with stress, whereas children are more likely to break down under pressure, especially during a crisis. When children observe their parents handling a situation maturely and in a positive frame of mind, they will be more secure. Children who face difficulties become more resilient. Keeping children away from reality will not shelter them from danger; rather, they should learn by taking the bull by the horns, with adult guidance. Parents and guardians should provide an environment of trust, encouraging them to share their fears and insecurities.

Children see the uptick in COVID-19 cases and recognize its association with death. They also understand that the current situation leads to more restrictions such as lockdowns. The increase in social isolation with the uncertainty of the COVID-19 crisis is having a profound effect on children. Other factors are: guns being bought and stored at the domicile, school-provided iPads enhancing search engine queries on how to commit suicide, insomnia exacerbating impulse control, irresponsible gaming, and, quite simply, hopelessness. It's practically inevitable we are going to observe an increase in adolescent suicides. We will never know all the facts, but the lockdowns are fueling social isolation and economic downturns, all contributing to mental illness.

Even after the COVID-19 crisis has passed, the lingering effects of the pandemic will not just go away. The realities of the school environment will surround the kids who have spent a year in their homes. The world's health and education leaders must focus on helping young people get past these dark times. Groups like Suicide Awareness Voices of Education, Voices of Education, and government agencies are providing qualified health workers to monitor and report emotional issues among children. A more detailed analysis may eventually reveal a more complex association between youth suicide and COVID-19. In light of the above, a need exists for governments to undertake a comprehensive study, in partnership with health care professionals, to identify issues that restrict children's ability to communicate honestly (and without fear) their emotional concerns with their families or counselors. Many parents hesitate to associate the suicides with school closings because it goes against the dominant narrative. Parents seem hesitant to connect their children's mental illness with school closures. Many parents who have lost their children to suicide during the lockdowns say they are sharing their story in hopes of it preventing another young death.

Addressing children's psychological needs is complex, and they need professional help to avert disastrous consequences such as depression or suicide. Children who are emotionally withdrawn or depressed should immediately receive psychiatric help. Prominent warning signs for parents are an increase in irritability, withdrawal, a lack of engagement in activities, problems with concentration, changes in eating and sleeping patterns, and addiction to video games, or any substances.

A happy childhood lays the foundation for a bright and secure future, and this pandemic too shall pass. However, it is important to ensure that it does not leave indelible scars on the minds of the children; but rather, it helps equip them with resilience, coping mechanisms, and the essential support network which will hold them in good stead over the long run.

## Case: Adolescent girl - Anonymous

This is an interesting case study of a young 14-year-old girl with severe depression, suicidality, chronic headaches, PTSD, post-concussion syndrome, and neuropathic leg pain resulting from a traumatic fall:

*She failed multiple antidepressant and analgesic modalities and presented to a hospital with suicidal ideation. While in the hospital, all of her exams and tests came back normal. She has spent two months in the hospital previously for depression and suicidality having attempted suicide multiple times in the past with a shoestring and pillow cover. She tried just about every medication available to ease her leg pain: non-steroidal anti-inflammatory agents, acetaminophen, antidepressants, gabapentinoids, anti-seizure medications, and opioid medications. She even had CBT and epidural steroid injections. The doctors tried everything to control this child's pain without success. During this hospital admission, they gave her an intravenous ketamine infusion for one week. On day one, her pain numerical rating scale (NRS) was 7/10. After being on a ketamine infusion for 24 hours, her pain NRS score was a little lower at 5/10. Her mood improved significantly, and she had no further suicidal ideation. On day three, the child's pain NRS score was still 5/10, and on day four, the NRS score was 4/10. She had functional movement in her leg because the pain was decreased. On day five, her pain NRS score was a 0/10 and her mood was markedly improved. For the first time, she could take part in physical therapy without pain. Her psychiatric reassessment determined her to be no longer at suicide risk, and she was released from the hospital with follow-up to her outpatient psychiatrist. Her relief lasted for nearly six months until she was readmitted because of a suicide attempt. She was again given an intravenous ketamine infusion, and she experienced the same relief as before.*

*Source: Weber G, et al. Case Report of Subanesthetic dose of Intravenous Ketamine Infusion for the Treatment of Neuropathic Pain and Depression with Suicidal Features in a Pediatric Patient. Case Rep Anesthesiol. 2018.*

Even in normal circumstances, suicides are impulsive and unpredictable, and it can be difficult to find a specific cause. Millions of students have relied on schools for mental-health services that are now restricted. Many psychiatrists acknowledge that the COVID-19 crisis is affecting the mental-health of children and adolescents. Hospitalizations for youth suicidal behaviors and suicide attempts have nearly doubled since 2008. Untreated depression can be detrimental and leads to developmental problems.

Experiencing the death of a loved one, especially a parent, is the most disruptive and stressful event a child can experience. Approximately 1 in 20 adolescents lose someone to suicide annually, and roughly 1 in 5 do so before reaching adulthood. Common grief reactions include crying and feelings of sadness, guilt, and longing. Although the grief following any type of death may be similar, some features may be more pronounced after a suicide. Death differentiates you from your peers, visibly demonstrated by increasing feelings of being alone. Common reactions in adolescents grieving a loved one lost to suicide included feelings of shock, sadness, guilt, injustice, anger, betrayal, struggling with questions of "why," and worrying over the impact of the death on others. For most young participants, the death seems incomprehensible. It impacts the family equilibrium and ability to support each other. Parental loss during adolescence results in anxiety, depression, and substance abuse. Long-term developmental competencies, such as educational and work aspirations, are diminished in the aftermath of parental suicide. For a child, death by suicide is the most confusing way to lose someone. The grief following a suicide is experienced more like a death of a traumatic or homicidal nature by adolescents and adults alike. Subtle triggers unrelated to the death or the deceased person (e.g., a song on the radio) can ambush the bereaved adolescent. One child said, "when you lose someone through suicide and when you're a kid, you don't really know what's going on. You are so confused, because you're just left with so many questions, many of which consist of "Why," "What if," and "How?" For most young people, the bereavement of a suicide or other traumatic death is a new and radical experience, for which they have not yet developed a language. One mom said, "My daughter couldn't say how she was feeling. All she could say was, 'I have feelings'." They look, sound, and seem to be the same person who they were before, but they're not; because while they've experienced the same loss as you, they've experienced it differently.

# HEALTH CARE PROFESSIONAL SUICIDE

Health care workers are dying of suicide at surprising rates. Historically, doctors commit suicide at a rate of 400 per year, the same statistic for nurses being even higher. Despite their often-hero-compared status, health care workers are vulnerable to post-traumatic stress. Doctors and nurses practice in a profession that encourages "toughing it out" and "not complaining." Health care workers are susceptible to depression and suicide; despite access to mental-health resources, we are witnessing elevated suicide rates among medical professionals serving at the frontlines of the battle against COVID-19. In New York, for example, a Bronx EMT shot himself with a gun belonging to his father, a retired NYPD officer.

The story of Dr. Lorna Breen, the director of a Manhattan hospital emergency department, is especially relevant:

## Case: Lorna Breen

Dr. Breen's hospital was overwhelmed with an influx of COVID-19 patients. Returning from vacation on March 14th, she was confronted with issues like inadequate personal protective equipment and lack of ventilators. Four days later she tested positive for COVID-19 and self-quarantined at home to recover. In a period of three weeks, Dr. Breen had treated patients with COVID-19, contracted the virus herself, recovered, and returned to work.

On April 1st, her first day back on the job, she faced a colossal workload, including back-to-back fifteen-hour days, with patients dying in the hallways, and experiencing post-COVID symptoms from which she herself was still suffering. She and her colleagues worked with limited protection, hospital beds, and lack of resources. She was simultaneously covering two hospitals five miles from each other. On April 4th, Dr. Breen was already showing signs of stress. A Bible study colleague stated she had never seen Dr. Breen in "such a state." She was in a war zone. It was as bad as everyone heard - there were intubated patients on stretchers jammed in the hallways, a shortage of oxygen tanks, and the radiology department was serving as a hospice center for patients dying COVID-19. It was a seemingly impossible situation. Dr. Breen knew she could not help patients the way she wanted, and quitting was not an option. During the peak of the pandemic, nearly a quarter of all people admitted to the emergency department with COVID-19 would die.

On April 9th, 2020, sounding unlike herself, Dr. Breen called her sister from her Manhattan apartment, reporting that she could not even get up from a chair. She was nearly catatonic and was uttering only two-word sentences, if you could even call them that. A chain of friends and family drove her to Charlottesville, Virginia, where she was admitted to a psychiatric ward for 11 days.

On April 21st, Dr. Breen left the hospital. Things seemed better. She started going out for long runs. However, five days later, she took her own life. She died of self-inflicted wounds at the University of Virginia Hospital.

The tragic case of Dr. Breen is interesting, because she had no prior history of mental illness, depression, or anxiety. Intelligent and motivated, her commitment and drive were impressive. She was enrolled in the Cornell executive M.B.A. / M.S. health care leadership degree. Most of us do not think we will be gone from this earth by the age of 49. To better understand her suicide and why the COVID-19 crisis played such a crucial role, it is both important and relevant to consider Dr. Breen's life before the COVID-19 crisis.

Lorna Breen came from a family of doctors and lawyers. Yearning to become a doctor from an early age, she graduated from the Wyoming Seminary Class in 1988. Dr. Breen was a consummate overachiever, graduating from medical school and completing two residencies - internal and emergency medicine. She spent as much time in residency as many neurosurgeons - 18 years of education after high school. During her residency, Dr. Breen's colleagues described her as someone who could pull an overnight shift and still appear fresh the next morning.

According to her friends, she took rigid viewpoints, as many doctors do. It is not a stretch to assume Dr. Breen was a perfectionist. She was always learning. She was an avid snowboarder and marathon runner who enjoyed playing cello in an orchestra and salsa dancing. Dr. Breen had to put her life on hold when COVID-19 hit.

Flashing forward to March, when she returned from her vacation. The stress, insomnia, and anxiety took their toll on her. She spent a week and a half at home and then insisted on going back to work, but something changed. Her family notes, "Something about her was not there." Although she had no apparent history of severe depression, it's arguable Dr. Breen displayed symptoms after the COVID-19 infection. Her father, a well-respected trauma surgeon, explained in a television show interview that she was not the same after the infection.

So what was it, after the COVID-19 infection that caused her to have a mental breakdown requiring admission to a psychiatric institution? Perhaps if the culture were different, doctors could reveal when they are suffering with mental illness instead of repressing, ignoring, or hiding their symptoms. Doctors are comfortable diagnosing and treating trauma but are reluctant to reveal their own mental-health issues for fear of ruining their careers.

Health-care workers are struggling to cope and facing unprecedented challenges: inadequate personal protective equipment, exposure to family members, sick colleagues, overwhelmed facilities, fear of medical board punishment, and work stress.

Finally, consider that even medical professionals who are familiar with mental-health resources seldom ask for help. Imagine the impact upon people who don't know about the resources, recognize the warning signs, and get help. Dr. Breen's family has set up a foundation to raise awareness about physician burnout and to safeguard their well-being (https://drlornabreen.org/)

## U.S. VETERANS AND SUICIDE

Veterans commit suicide at nearly double the rate of the general population; around 20 service members and veterans die by suicide in the U.S. each day, or 6,000 per year. Since ancient times, military organizations have trained professional soldiers to use physical force to defend their society against the enemy. The inherent risk of injury and death from war exposes veterans to severe physical and mental trauma. Soldiers use weapons to kill both others and themselves, and the reasons veterans commit suicide are not different from those of anyone else. A 2012 study questioned 72 veterans who attempted suicide, and every one of them spoke about their desire to end the intense emotional distress.

Veterans own more guns than others and often use a firearm to commit suicide. They return home from a last tour of duty, where they have faced combat and extreme, often violent, experiences, to find themselves isolated and alone. Most who commit suicide do so within a year of leaving the military. The loss of more than 60,000 veterans to suicide over the last decade is a tragically high number. A report from the 2012 study revealed that nearly 70 percent of veterans who ended their lives by suicide had not recently received health care services from the Department of Veterans Affairs.

Governments rarely hesitate to spend money to send soldiers to war, but they do falter in paying for the problems soldiers encounter upon returning home. The Veterans Administration (VA) hospital system is a vivid example of this. Soldiers returning from combat often experience difficulties in getting appropriate mental-health care within the VA hospital system. Thousands of veteran's experience delays in treatment and many die by suicide while waiting for their care. The COVID-19 crisis has contributed to these delays.

Hillary Clinton was famously quoted as saying many surveys show veterans were satisfied with the VA medical care. This is not the sentiment the majority of soldiers express. In fairness, much like socialized medicine, the VA provides excellent care for emergencies such as heart attacks or dealing with cancer, but a problem emerges when it comes to confronting mental-health care concerns.

Reducing veteran suicide is a top priority for the VA. In March 2019, then President Trump rolled out an executive order known as the President's Road Map to Empower Veterans and End a National Tragedy of Suicide (PREVENTS), billed as eleven different governmental departments and private firms formed a task force where the goal to create a research strategy to study the factors that contribute to veteran suicide. The task force was delayed because of the COVID-19 crisis. The goals of the initiative were to increase awareness that suicide is both preventable and treatable. It encouraged employers and academic institutions to not only provide mental-health and wellness practices, but to increase suicide-prevention training. The task force recommended funding suicide-prevention programs at the federal level.

Traumatic military experiences play a contributing role in suicide. For example, combat exposure, injury, bereavement, negative unit climate, family-related stressors, as well as physical, sexual, financial, and acute health problems, are all common stress-related circumstances occurring prior to suicidal ideation. Combat exposure causes significant prolonged stress, requiring many of those deployed to be on constant guard from any unfriendly fire, improvised explosive devices (IEDs), and other dangers while patrolling civilian areas. The prolonged and repeated nature of deployments, along with the uncertainty about whether one's tour will be extended, creates a significant burden on soldiers and their families. All this culminates in PTSD. As many as 13 percent of combat veterans have PTSD. In 2018, the U.S. Department of Veteran Affairs spent 17 billion dollars on disability payments for over one million veterans with PTSD. For the approximately half to one-third of people who do not find relief through treatment, PTSD can become a chronic and debilitating disease, sometimes lasting a lifetime.

Wounded soldiers have an increased risk of suicide and need extra support. Medical advances have created new life-saving interventions, which extend survival in the face of serious injuries. However, combat survivors with injuries are more likely to commit suicide. Paradoxically, those who survive horrific injuries are left alone to deal with their serious health problems including disabilities and disfigurements. Traumatic brain injury (TBI) is a particular flag for suicide risk among military populations.

A subject seldom discussed, is the fact that there is a high prevalence of TBI among military personnel because of the widespread exposure to IEDs and blast injuries resulting in head trauma. Traumatic brain injury can cause an increased risk of depression and PTSD. The neuro-psychological consequences of traumatic brain injury include aggression, disinhibition, impulsivity, and suicide. Military tribalism is another seldom discussed reality. Soldiers in combat often exhibit a strong tribal mentality. These soldiers are tasked with protecting each other every day in difficult situations. Some of the strongest bonds are forged during combat. Humans, as primates, desire to belong and become connected to groups. Military soldiers in combat will sacrifice, kill, and die for their group. Once a soldier leaves the group environment, there is a sense of losing one's identity, and this can lead to mental illness.

The military has recently employed screening tools for pre-existing psychological disorders called Comprehensive Soldier Fitness, representing the Army's decision to place an equal emphasis on psychological / mental strength as on physical strength. Soldiers are recruited younger nowadays, and many are present with psychological disorders, especially those exposed to war. Basic training, sleep deprivation, loss of family support, foreign environment, combat, and anxiety about deployment all increase the stressors related to this population. Screening for mental disorders is a promising avenue for preventing some suicides. Still, it is important to remember having a mental disorder alone does not predict suicidal behavior: and equally, many of those who do commit suicide had no history of mental-health issues. Military screening efforts to determine risk include constructing exercises to elevate the distress a person goes through in response to negative situations such as hand-to-hand combat. Also, the ability to solve problems, seek help through adaptive methods, and assessing the likelihood of acting on impulses to escape from undesirable situations, are methods employed by the military. Despite these positive steps, real progress on the issue of suicide among veterans is still out of reach.

## Case: Navy Seal and Afghanistan veteran - anonymous

*My ketamine treatment was unlike anything I've ever experienced. I'm still processing it and trying to quantify the benefits period. First, the facility was first-class and conducive to a very positive experience. The treatment room was modern and comfortable. I was briefed on the procedure and given assurances that the treatment was safe and controlled. At the start of the treatment, I felt very peaceful and lighthearted. Having a board-certified anesthesiologist and family in the room gave me added assurance, which became increasingly meaningful as the treatment progressed. I closed my eyes and tried to relax and enjoy the tranquility. I quickly drifted off and was taken into what seemed to be another dimension. It felt like I was traveling upwards, often without a sense of gravity or time, and my surroundings were constantly changing as if walls were folding in on themselves. As I continued deeper in these dimensions, I wondered at times how I would return. That's where knowing a trusted family member being present became important. Even though I had seemingly lost touch with reality, I knew someone was there to bring me back eventually. At several points during the experience, I thought I was fully awake and back in the treatment room, only to find myself drifting off into another dream world. As I began to come back to reality, I continued to drift in and out of the dream world, but I was relieved to come back to the real world finally. I felt a sense of relief and happiness knowing I was safely back home with my family members who were waiting for me in the treatment room. As I continue to process the experience, the primary takeaway was the sense of happiness that I was back home with my family and in control of my life. This may have a very beneficial therapeutic effect for those who have lost appreciation for the things we often take for granted, like family, being alive, and having control of your life.*

## Case: Mike Donnelly

*U.S. military veteran Mike Donnelly's talks about how ketamine treatments have helped him. Because of his combat experiences and suffering from PTSD while serving with the Army National Guard in Iraq, he found himself at the "end of my rope." He tried to find help via the internet and the VA hospital system. Failing conventional medical therapy because of the side effects, he began to have feelings of hopelessness and increasing frustration with the VA medical system. He describes a situation familiar to many service members afflicted with PTSD encounter who have reached out to the VA medical system for psychiatric disorders. Mike managed as best he could for years and found himself on the brink of suicide when he walked into a VA hospital in West Haven, Connecticut, and asked to see someone about his issues. He was given a 1-800 number to call for suicide prevention, a "pat on the back," and was told to come back in a month to see how the medications were working. From that point, he explains that he spent six months trying to find the correct medicines at the proper dosage with little relief. He could not function as a father, husband, or employee and was destroying his and close friendships as well. It was he was contemplating suicide or not, and he was planning to use his firearm. His depression was profound, and he dove into self-help books and religion. He stumbled upon a video about ketamine treatment that claimed to help PTSD symptoms.*

*He found a physician named Dr. Ang in Connecticut but unfortunately the cost of the treatment was prohibitive because his insurance denied any coverage for ketamine treatments. From this point, he recalls barely being able to get out of bed, take a shower and eat. He sold a prized rifle to raise the money needed for the ketamine treatments, which he later reflected as a good decision. Mike went through with the ketamine treatments and secured financial support through the foundation called the Ketamine Fund. Mike regained a better life with himself, and his family, which essentially saved his life. He even lost his job during the COVID-19 crisis and handled it well.*

Source: The Ketamine Fund website and personal communication with Zappy Zapolin and Warren Gumpel, 2021.

## FIRST RESPONDER SUICIDES

After a routine shift, 28-year-old Richland County Sheriff, Derek Fish, returned to his cruiser and shot himself with his service revolver. In response to this incident, Leon Lott, a fellow Richland County Sheriff, expressed the dire need for a change in how law enforcement addresses suicide and mental-health problems.

No federal agency officially counts the number of suicides in the law-enforcement community. The National Police Suicide Foundation (NPS) is devoted to preventing suicide by promoting suicide awareness and prevention training programs.

First responder (police officers, firefighters, etc.) suicide is complex. A recent study in 2017 found that police officers and firefighters are far more likely to die by suicide than in the line of duty. According to the study there were at least 103 firefighter suicides and 140 police officer suicides. In contrast, 93 firefighters and 129 police officers died in the line of duty. In 2020, at least 228 police officers died by suicide, whereas 132 officers died in the line of duty; this is a 25 percent increase from 2019. Mainstream media outlets seldom cover first responder suicides, and the public remains unaware of the issue. They do not consider first responder suicides as "line-of-duty deaths" and surviving families often receive no financial compensation. Approximately 90 percent of police officers who commit suicide in the U.S. do so with a firearm. Limiting access to these weapons is not feasible when considering an officer's need for them in the field. Most suicides are traced to depression and PTSD, which stems from constant exposure to death and violence.

Sociological factors come into play as well. Many cultural barriers and personality traits exist within the men and women who become first responders. One barrier preventing first responders from accessing necessary mental-health services is a culture of prioritizing bravery and toughness. This also increases the lack of awareness regarding the mental-health of first responders. However, first responders experience heightened levels of depression, PTSD, suicidal thoughts, and more.

There needs to be a more open discussion about mental illness among the first responder community, including firefighters and police offices. Suicide is the most catastrophic of consequences for failing to treat mental illness. Police officers and firefighters often experience PTSD and depression but feel the need to hide mental-health challenges because of the aforementioned cultural stigma. In police departments, a code of secrecy exists around mental illness. The topic is uneasy to talk about or approach. One officer reported,

*"When I was involved in my first shooting, I was cleared right away and I was not given any administrative time off. Basically, they bought you a beer and told you that you were a hero. I had to deal with it all on my own, and there were no department resources or even a chaplain."*

It is surprising, and shocking, that more officers die by their own hands than by other causes. More officers have died of suicide than shootings and traffic accidents combined. Among the 228 police officers who died by suicide in 2020, approximately 25 percent were veterans with at least 20 years of service. Work-related stress and depression are commonplace in police work. It's tough, especially in large cities like New York City or St. Louis. Police suicide is also frequent in other countries like Ireland, the U.K., and Australia. Law enforcement is among the most harrowing career fields in the world - consider the strain involved in dealing with criminals and victims of accidents, verbal and physical abuse, gang violence, murder, and suicide. The sheer volume of negative memories can be catastrophic.

Some organizations have recommended police officers receive some type of mental-health care annually from a therapist who is versed in dealing with first responder stress and trauma. One officer with 24 years of police service describes how he found himself alone in his bedroom with his gun drawn and ready to shoot himself. Luckily, his wife walked in and kept him from going through with the suicide. They diagnosed him with PTSD and depression, and he started both therapy and medication.

The recent Washington D.C. Capitol riots were a stark reminder of a country divided. Few realize that two Washington D.C. officers committed suicide shortly after the riots. Officers Jeffery Smith and Harold Liebengood, two 12- and 15-year veterans, respectively, in the Washington D.C. Police Department, committed suicide after the riots. On January 6th, at 2:38 p.m. Officer Smith sent his wife a text, "London has fallen." This was in response to the start of the Capitol riots and a reference to a movie about a plan to assassinate world leaders attending a funeral in Britain. Along with 850 other D.C. police officers, Jeffery Smith took part in the January 6th Capitol riots where over 70 officers were injured. Around 5:35 p.m., he was in the Capitol building fighting the rioters, when they hurled a metal pole that struck his helmet and face shield. He continued working into the night. At 9 p.m., he told two supervisors he was in pain from being hit by the pole and later visited the police medical clinic at 10:15 p.m. On his police injury form he wrote: "Hit with a flying object in face shield and helmet" and "Began feeling pain in my neck and face." He left the clinic at 1:31 a.m., was placed on sick leave and sent home with pain medications. According to his wife in a Washington Post interview, Smith seemed in constant pain and was unable to turn his head. He did not leave the house or go outside to walk their dog as he had usually done. He refused to talk to other people or watch television and spoke little about the riots. His wife described him in the days that followed as dealing with insomnia, waking during the night, and pacing about. Mrs. Smith says, *"He was not the same Jeff that left on the 6th…"* On January 14th, Smith returned to the police clinic for a follow-up appointment and was ordered back to work. The next afternoon, he left the house for an overnight shift, taking the ham-and-turkey sandwiches his wife had packed. On his way to the District, Smith used his firearm to shoot himself in the head.

One politician, Rep. Jamie B. Raskin (D-Md.), aware that two officers had taken their lives after the Capitol riots, was also the lead manager at Trump's impeachment trial. Sadly, Rep. Raskin buried his 25-year-old son, Tommy Raskin, the day before the Capitol riots took place. Tommy Raskin had committed suicide on New Year's Eve.

# PART TWO:
# THE SCIENCE

# CHAPTER SIX:
## WHY DOES SUICIDE OCCUR?

*"At our base, humans are survival machines.*
*We are robotic vehicles blindly programmed to*
*preserve the selfish molecules known as genes."*
—Dawkins, The Selfish Gene.

## THE HIDDEN SIDE OF SUICIDE

Often, there are no warning signs, and you may wonder what clues you might have missed. Suicide affects all men, women, and children. A multitude of factors drives a person to the decision to commit suicide. Most who experience suicidal thoughts have them for the first time in their early 20s. Predicting who will be affected is difficult. When suicidal thoughts occur, the transition to a suicide attempt happens quickly, suggesting the need for rapid intervention. Suicidal behaviors are complex. In order to study suicidal behavior in a detailed manner, large samples of people are required.

Survivors of suicide attempts often describe the experience as if their own brains had been ambushed by their negative internal monologue, which emphasizes the pointlessness of existence.

> ### Case: Steve
>
> *Steve is an aerospace engineer, and entrepreneur who loves living life to its fullest. Months prior, he had been involved in a bicycle crash where he sustained a severe traumatic brain injury (TBI) and, as a result, underwent several surgeries. Steve called his physician and asked if he had 30 minutes to talk. He spoke in a concerned and unusual voice, describing the night not long*

*before when he had attempted suicide. Steve remembers walking furiously through the desert in the middle of the night; he was on a mission to take his life. His goal was to find a place next to a tree and to deliberately fall on his knife. He had it all planned out for several weeks - where to put the knife in the ground, how to fall on it, and the best time of night he needed to complete his task. He had researched the fastest method of self-exsanguination (bleeding out) in order to take his life.*

*Steve emphasized he felt as if he had little control over his suicide attempt. It was as if his brain had hijacked his emotions. However, when that final moment in the desert came, he could not bring himself to fall on that knife. In fact, this was Steve's second attempt to take his life, and he nearly succeeded. Steve was experiencing major depression from his TBI. Suicidal behavior is common after major head trauma.*

*Steve was given ketamine, and his motivation to kill himself subsided. This bought him some time to seek help for his depression and traumatic brain injury, and he eventually overcame his condition. Since then, he has never had thoughts of suicide.*

Only humans commit suicide. We can choose to take our own lives, where other animals will not premeditate the end of their own lives, at least not in the way that we think about suicide. Our brains enable us to allow or inhibit impulses, emotional reactions, select a choice of behavioral responses, delay gratification, and much more. We process immense amounts of information through the human cortex, which controls executive function. This prevents us from reacting to impulses that come from the lower brain, an important human evolutionary advance.

Natural selection shapes our emotions to maximize the survival of the species. We are only about 300 generations removed from our Stone-Age ancestors. Genetics play a strong role in why we commit suicide as suggested from twin studies. Evolutionary psychiatry teaches us that mother nature does not care whether we feel good or bad. We are inherently programmed through our DNA to preserve and propagate our existence – explained by the selfish gene theory. Genes are dynamic contributors to our behavioral organization and are sensitive to the feedback systems from our internal and external environments. Technically, behavior is not inherited, only our genes are inherited. After birth, our behaviors are shaped through the constant interplay between genetic potential and our environment. Emotions, anxiety, and depression all have an evolutionary benefit. Today, there seems to be a mismatch between our ancient emotional wiring and how we live in society.

Suicide is one of the leading causes of death globally. In 2018, ten million people thought about suicide, three million planned to commit suicide, one million actually attempted suicide, and sadly, close to eight hundred thousand people died from suicide. Ten million Americans report they have unmet mental-health needs. Emergency room visits relating to mental-health crises have increased by nearly 50 percent during the COVID-19 crisis. Why have so many people contemplated suicide, and why have we seen such an increase? We have no simple answers, but idea of suicide is invariably multifaceted. Half of all people who die by suicide have no known mental-health conditions at their time of death. Research has shown that depression is firmly correlated with suicide; about 78 percent of suicides are preceded by an untreated psychiatric illness. Another important factor is substance abuse, which is causally related to suicide. Opioid-related deaths from overdoses and suicides by other methods have been higher during the COVID-19 crisis.

## A BRIEF HISTORY OF DEPRESSION AND SUICIDE

Suicide and depression have always been a part of humanity. Tracing suicide's history through time is useful. The earliest accounts of suicide and depression appear in Mesopotamia, some 2000 years B.C. Mental illness was seen as a religious matter, and methods for treating depression included beatings, physical restraints, and starvation to "drive" demons out. The Romans and Greeks had more pragmatic attitudes towards the concept of suicide. In contrast, the Christians viewed suicide as a mortal sin, as outlined by St. Thomas Aquinas (c. 1225 - 1274).

"Therefore, to kill oneself is contrary to natural inclination, and contrary to the charity according to which everyone ought to love himself."

For example, if a man committed suicide with a knife, his hand would be cut off and punished separately, and the knife would then be banished and thrown beyond the city walls. The ancient Greeks and Romans introduced the concept that depression and suicide are biologically associated, coining the term "melancholia." Persian physicians wrote about mental illness arising from the brain. They believed melancholy to be caused by an imbalance of body fluids called humors (yellow bile, black bile, phlegm, and blood). Hippocrates believed melancholia was derived from an excess of black bile, and his treatments included bloodletting, baths, exercise, and diet. Along with Hippocrates' treatments, doctors from these times used baths, bloodletting, diet, donkey's milk, leeches, massage, sex, poppy extracts, and meditation.

The medieval mind was caught between the ignorance of the Dark Ages and the illumination of the Renaissance. Despite advances in medicine, it was still a common belief that demons and the anger of the gods caused depression. During the Middle Ages, Christianity dominated European thinking on mental illness, with people again attributing it to the devil, demons, and witches. During the 15th century Renaissance and into the 17th century, public burnings, drownings, and exorcisms were widespread. The term "lunatic asylums" - became popular. Many innocent women were burned alive at the stake due to postpartum depression. Ideas about suicide began shifting after the Renaissance period. In the early 17th century, Burton, a physician, published the "*Anatomy of Melancholy*" outlining the social and psychological causes of depression and suicide such as fear, loneliness, and poverty. Burton recommended methods to clear toxins from the body through bloodletting, diet, exercise, herbs, music, and travel. Archaic treatments such as water immersion (waterboarding) and centrifugal force (spinning stools) "to put the brain" contents back into their correct place were used.

The period known as "The Enlightenment promoted" changes in medicine and engineering and allowed the first suggestions of psychotherapy during this period. U.S. inventor Benjamin Franklin developed an ancient form of electroshock therapy. By the late 1800s, depression and the act of suicide was thought to be a permanent inheritable illness, rather than a moral sin.

### Suicide: A Judicial or a Medical Issue?

In the early 1900s, suicide was illegal. It was considered a judicial rather than a medical problem. English law distinguished between suicide and homicide. The following English account of the Ashby case illustrates this point:

On June 25, 1914, in the small coastal town of Lowestoft, England, 59-year-old Louisa Ashby cuts her own throat with a razor and lay down on her bed. Her granddaughter discovers her covered in blood and ran to inform her mother "grandmother had cut her finger." They rushed Louisa to the nearby North Suffolk hospital. The hospital matron requests a police officer stay and take sole charge and responsibility for Ms. Ashby. The matron accuses the police of not doing his duty, saying the woman has committed attempted murder, and should be charged. The hospital matron even threatened to take Ashby and put her outside the hospital gates. Louisa Ashby dies two days later.

The tragic Ashby case is an indication of just how far we have come in recognizing and treating suicide. The idea of "self-harm" as we presently understand it did not exist in 1914. Terms such as self-cutting, self-mutilation, flesh-picking and self-biting were not emphasized in 19th-century writings. In the case of Louisa Ashby, the police were reluctant to charge her with the offense of attempting suicide because that would involve taking responsibility for that person. Suicide and attempted suicide were illegal in England and Wales until 1961. The 1930 Mental Treatment Act was considered the starting point for the integration of general and mental medicine in Britain.

Source: A history of self-harm in Britain, 2015

In the 20th century, German psychiatrist Emil Kraepelin became the first to define manic depression, today known as bipolar disorder. In 1917, Sigmund Freud wrote about melancholia as being a response to death, loss, or failures and was among the first to use psychoanalysis to treat mental disorders. Freud developed a theory that consciousness leads to self-hatred and destructive behavior. The behaviorist movement in psychology contributed to the thinking that behaviors are learned rather than inherited. The behaviorists rejected Freud's theories that depression was caused by unconscious forces.

During the 1960s, cognitive theories of depression emerged. Psychologist Aaron Beck, founder of cognitive behavioral therapy (CBT) and the Beck Depression Inventory (BDI), discovered that depressed patients often experienced spontaneous negative thoughts about themselves, the world, and others. In the 1970s, biological models of mental disorders emerged; thus, so did the use of pharmaceuticals to treat them. Biological explanations focused on brain chemistry, anatomy, genetics, and hormones. The treatment of tuberculosis with isoniazid in the 1950s was pivotal in the treatment of depression. People treated with isoniazid reported an immediate lifting of their depression, leading to the discovery of drugs like Prozac. This paved the way to over 50 years of using antidepressants like Prozac to treat severe depression.

Lobotomies, a surgery intended to destroy part of the frontal lobe, were once popular for the treatment of mental disorders. Italian psychiatrist, Ugo Cerletti introduced electroconvulsive therapy (ECT) in 1938, which eventually replaced lobotomies. Even today, ECT remains the gold standard for treating severe depression. Lithium was also used for bipolar disorder and suicide prevention. Advances in the understanding of depression have resulted in newer effective treatments: transcranial magnetic stimulation (TMS), vagus nerve stimulation, and ketamine. These treatments will be explained later.

We can categorize the reasons humans commit suicide into mental illness, financial crises, traumatic stress, substance abuse, fear of loss, hopelessness, chronic pain and disease, social isolation, and a "cry for help." Many factors lead a person to the decision to take his/her own life. Suicidal behavior often presents with feelings of hopelessness and worthlessness, of not wanting to be a burden to others or an unwillingness to suffer unbearable pain. Many suicidal people speak openly and often about killing themselves.

## MENTAL ILLNESS

The choice to attempt suicide is often made impulsively, rather than through extensive planning. Non-verbal behavior, isolation, withdrawal, excessive sleeping, substance abuse, increased agitation, and anxiousness are signs that a person may want to commit suicide. The most common cause influencing a person's decision to commit suicide is severe depression. Depression causes people to feel intense hopelessness, making them unable to see any other way to relieve their emotional pain outside of suicide.

## ACCESS TO MENTAL-HEALTH CARE

The lockdowns have affected access to mental-health care. The high rates of suicide in American Indian and Alaskan communities are due, in part, to a lack of culturally relevant mental-health care. Rural and remote communities have less access to this kind of mental-health care and may experience higher rates of suicide.

Evidence suggests that suicide in veterans is partially due to a lack of mental-health care providers who can specifically relate to military training and being deployed in war. As discussed above, the increase in veteran suicides has resulted in many U.S. legislators increasing their funding for "gatekeeper training" programs.

Laypersons could be trained to interact with those at risk for suicide, giving them the means to refer these people to mental-health support services. For example, in some states, first aid responders and teachers receive mental-health care training. Gatekeeper training is gaining popularity, for example, Utah has created hotlines that connect licensed mental-health professionals using a smartphone application. Efforts to expand services by federally mandating private insurance to cover mental-health have been passed, but the enforcement of these laws is left to the states.

## TRAUMATIC STRESS

Domestic-violence deaths have more than doubled in 2020 compared with previous years. Adverse childhood trauma, abuse (both physical and sexual), and rape, greatly increase the risk for suicide, even years after the actual event. In a survey involving people who survived physical assault, nearly one-quarter of those interviewed thought about taking their own life at some point. Being diagnosed with PTSD and depression raises the risk of suicide even further. This is partly because depression is common after trauma; and among those with PTSD, feelings of hopelessness often lead to suicidal behaviors.

In schools, bullying, shaming, and humiliation place children at an increased risk for suicide, especially in LGBTQ adolescent populations. At least 25 percent of all transgender adolescents have attempted suicide. It is the second leading cause of death for LGBTQ youth aged 15 to 24. Cyberbullying has caused many child, adolescent, and adult suicides;

when directly or indirectly linked to suicide, this has been referred to as cyberbullicide. While these children have not been subject to the same bullying as a result of classrooms shifting from physical to virtual, the element of bullying still remains. While on social networking platforms, cyberbullying has taken its toll on people's mental-health.

## SUBSTANCE ABUSE, FIREARMS, AND IMPULSIVITY

Half of the United States has seen an increase in suicides greater than 30 percent and is now the second-leading cause of death for those ages 10 to 34, (accidents are the leading cause). Growing economic disparities, lockdowns, easy access to guns, and the opioid crisis are all responsible for this. Decreasing our inhibitions increases the chance of acting on suicidal ideation: the COVID-19 crisis has intensified alcohol and substance abuse, significantly adding to suicide rates. Alcohol sales have increased by over 40 percent and firearm sales have increased by over 200 percent. Increasing the access to means of committing suicide will obviously increase the risk of dying in a suicide attempt. Males, especially veterans and police officers, die from suicide four times more often than women because of firearms. During the lockdowns, children forced to stay at home may discover unsecured firearms and die by suicide or simply by accident.

## HOPELESSNESS, SOCIAL ISOLATION, AND FEAR OF LOSS

During the COVID-19 crisis children are experiencing prolonged isolation from the lockdowns, which increases any existing stresses of being at home. Academic failure, loss of social status, financial problems, and the end of a romantic relationship can also lead to depression and suicide as can being arrested or imprisoned. In his book *Talking With Strangers*, Malcolm Gladwell eloquently relates how Sandra Blaine, a woman of color, was locked up after an escalated altercation with a white police officer during a traffic stop where she failed to use a turn signal. She committed suicide three days later in her jail cell.

People become socially isolated for many reasons including the loss of a spouse, partner, loved one, separation or divorce, physical or mental illness, social anxiety, retirement, or an unfamiliar environment. Those facing social or physical challenges cannot see a path to improve their situation and may resolve to end their life. Hopelessness is a common factor cited in many studies contributing to the ultimate decision to commit suicide. The 12-year-old Las Vegas boy cited hopelessness before he attempted suicide. When people feel they have lost all hope and cannot change their outlook, this can eclipse the positive aspects of their lives, making suicide seem like an option. Internal factors can cause social isolation such as low self-esteem, which could lead to loneliness, depression, and suicide. Socially-isolated people often use alcohol or drugs to mask their pain, which in turn decreases their inhibitions and increases their risk of suicide.

## CHRONIC PAIN AND DISEASE

People with chronic pain or illness often display suicidal behaviors because of a lack of hope or cure; loss of autonomy and ability to do enjoyable or meaningful activities; disease-related symptoms; fear of future suffering; or a lack of reprieve from their current suffering. For many, suicide may seem viable to control their life and maintain their dignity. In many countries, such as the Netherlands and Switzerland, assisted suicide is legal for this very reason.

Cancer, neurological disorders, and severe depression most commonly account for assisted suicides. Chronic pain is another factor leading to anxiety and depression and increases the risk of suicide. People with chronic pain and terminal illness often feel they are a burden to family members and friends because they require help with finances or household duties. They rationalize that life for those around them would be better off if they were gone. This type of rhetoric is a common warning sign of suicide.

## CRY FOR HELP

People sometimes want to show the world and those around them just how much they are suffering. These are not suicide attempts per se but are a cry for help. Some commit these acts not because they wish to die, but because they simply don't have a path to help. Many adolescent suicides are impulsive. Unfortunately, these cries for help can end fatally if the person misjudges the lethality of the chosen method, as often happens with medications. The Brandi Bielicki story from the previous chapter about her

10-year-old daughter's suicide is one such example.

## PSYCHOLOGY THEORIES OF SUICIDE

There are two general types of psychological factors that convey vulnerability to suicide risk. Subjectively reported psychological and temperamental factors such as depressive personality traits, impulsiveness, aggressiveness, or hopelessness about the future may predict vulnerability for suicide risk. Second, neuro-cognitive factors such as problems with decision making, problem solving, cognitive control, and verbal fluency also convey vulnerability for suicide risk.

Cognitive theories of suicidal behaviors are based on well-validated peer reviewed research. The interpersonal/psychological theory of suicidal behavior suggests that completed suicides require three specific characteristics: a sense of thwarted belongingness, a sense of burdensomeness, and a gained capability for suicide. The gained capability for suicide must be coupled with the reasons to attempt suicide. Different studies have reported psychiatric patients pay close attention to environmental cues that are specifically related to their suffering; in particular, the sense of hopelessness, burdensomeness, and loneliness, causing extreme difficulty, to finding solutions to their problems as an alternative to suicide.

Suicide is often an impulsive act, especially in adolescents. Impulsivity is partly controlled in the brain by the amygdala, which is the same part of the brain affected in attention deficit disorder.

The presence of a psychological disorder is among the most consistently reported risk factors for suicidal behavior. Autopsy studies of suicide victims reveal that over 90 percent have a diagnosable mental disorder at the time of their death. Comorbidity of mental illness is a major challenge for suicide prevention. For example, a history of major depression is one of the strongest predictors of suicidal ideation, but it does not predict actual suicide attempts. Therefore, it's important to distinguish between suicidal ideation and suicide attempts. Even more complex is the evidence most people with mental-health disorders never attempt suicide.

People with a family history of mental disorders and suicidal behavior may have an increased risk for suicidal behavior themselves. A parental history of panic disorder, antisocial personality disorder, and suicidal behavior predict suicidal behavior among offspring. Relating genetic factors to suicidal behaviors are promising, but it is difficult to reproduce these initial findings. Childhood adversities such as sexual and physical abuse often lead to subsequent suicidal behavior. Shared genetic and neuro-biological characteristics may explain this link between the parent and offspring. Especially when combined with a history of childhood abuse, parents who are impulsive and aggressive by nature are more likely to have children who are impulsive and aggressive as well. Both familial transmission of sexual abuse and/or impulsive aggression are potential mediators in the genetic transmission of suicidal behavior. Even studies of nonhuman primates reveal early infant experiences such as maternal deprivation contribute independently to the development of impulsive, aggressive, and self-injurious behavior.

Neurotransmitter imbalances of serotonin and the protein brain derived neurotrophic factor (BDNF) also appear to mediate this relationship. Current research is showing a strong association with the epigenetic regulations of genes that play a role in the human stress response system. Since you cannot choose your parents, it is essential to know that a person with a family history of mental disorders can overcome these difficulties through positive environmental factors and close productive relationships.

History of suicidal behavior is the strongest predictor of future suicide attempts and suicide death. Knowledge of prior suicidal behavior is invaluable in determining who is most at risk. People who have previous suicide attempts are nearly 40 times more likely to die by suicide than those without such a history. Multiple suicide attempts are associated with an increased risk of subsequent suicidal behavior, and often do so with increasing severity. So, if you have ever wondered why a nurse or a doctor asks you routinely if you are suicidal or have ever attempted suicide, this is the reason.

Suicide is difficult to study. Once someone dies of suicide, they can no longer provide information. Suicidal risk is very difficult to detect. One study found that 78 percent of suicidal people denied thoughts of suicide prior to killing themselves. It is important to distinguish between suicidal ideation, suicidal plans, suicidal attempts, and suicide death. Suicidal ideations are the serious thoughts about killing oneself. Suicidal plans are the formulations of an actual plot to kill oneself. Suicidal attempts are self-injurious behavior with an intent to die. Suicide death is the successful result of the final self-injurious action.

For over a century, psychiatrists have evaluated patients by asking them about their lives; and, while they are talking, the doctor carefully observes their speech and behavior. However, people with suicidal ideation can effectively hide their emotions. However, tools are being produced that may change this model. Social media has built an entire industry predicting a person's behavior based on their smartphone use and online activity. Our Internet searches and social-media history are time stamped and digitized, effectively leaving a breadcrumb trail of our thoughts and emotions. Psychiatrists are using this data to measure and evaluate our mental states as it may have extraordinary potential for psychiatric diagnosis and treatment of mental disorders.

Studies have shown that the words we use to express ourselves on social media can predict conditions like postpartum depression and psychosis. Digital tools help psychiatrists measure a patient's behavior during a therapy session. Speech and facial recognition technologies can be used to precisely measure a patient's expression, the words they use, and the intonation of their voice. Such tools can be used to recognize the subtle changes that occur when a patient becomes psychotic. For example, the frequency of possessive pronouns can predict with an accuracy of 83 percent whether someone is at risk for psychosis; decreased facial expressivity may also predict suicide. App-based therapies allow doctors to better connect with patients. Using artificial intelligence to quantify large amounts of data will help psychiatrists discover insights that are not necessarily intuitive.

Researchers must try to assemble information about the risk factors via the use of psychological autopsy methods and biochemical assays (tests). Even if the person survives the attempt, they are often unable or unwilling to report on the factors leading up to their suicidal behavior. People with mental-health problems often cannot report accurately on the factors influencing their behavior. Many people are simply unwilling to comment on the factors leading to their behavior. The fear of being institutionalized is one such reason. Also, many believe they do not have a problem, or doubt there is anything or anyone who can help them. Many do not want to receive any intervention. Lastly, many of those in professions such as the military, law enforcement, or members of the medical community fear disclosing such information for fear of losing their careers. These concerns create very real barriers and prevent those at risk from seeking help.

Matthew Nock, a Harvard psychologist, and a MacArthur Genius Award winner, has made advances in detecting suicide risk. He uses tools that look at unconscious bias, known in research as implicit association tests or IAT. An IAT test may show a series of pictures or words associated with death (suicide, gunshot, hanging, die, deceased, death) or life (alive, thrive, breathing, living) paired with pronouns or words related to self or other (I, myself, mine, they, themselves, their). A computer gives the test and asks subjects to sort the word pairs into categories associated with life or death. A large series of studies have shown that suicidal patients, even those who deny intent, have faster reaction times for pairs linking self-injury or death and self. The effect is so robust Nock and his team has developed a computer game to train patients to dissociate the connection between self-injury or death and self.

## COUPLING THEORY

The coupling theory states that suicide is a behavior connected to a particular context and specific circumstances. Suicide is not simply connected to a bout of severe depression. Rather, it is a severe depression in people who have a particular moment of extreme vulnerability combined with a readily available means to end their life. Malcolm Gladwell illustrates this in his book, *Talking With Strangers*. He points out that suicide is closely tied to the physical environment: when we look at a person as an individual, we cannot see their whole story. Instead, we should look at the whole picture, in a broader cultural and environmental context. Suicide is multifaceted, and there are many ways people get to that endpoint. They view their situation as a mechanical or engineering problem and see certain methods of fixing it. Gladwell highlights the example of suicide rates in 1960s Britain coupled with the availability of the commonly used "town gas." In the years after the Second World War, many British homes were heated using "town gas," which was a deadly mixture of hydrogen, methane, carbon dioxide, and, importantly, carbon monoxide. During this time, "town gas" suicide victims were frequently found with their heads wrapped in a blanket or a coat and a tube underneath pumping out the gas. Nearly

6,000 people committed suicide in Britain in 1962, with 2,500 using the town gas method. Pulitzer Prize-winning poet, Sylvia Plath was perhaps the most well-known case of this type of suicide.

> ### Case: Sylvia Plath
>
> *American poet, Sylvia Plath struggled with depression her entire life. Looking for a new start, she moved to England. In 1962, a period of sub-zero temperatures settled on England. Pipes froze solid, power outages occurred throughout the country, and many workers went on strike. That Christmas, she was sitting with her ex-husband having a glass of wine when they began arguing. Shortly after, she dismissed her maid, gathered her children and went to stay at a friend's house. She soon returned to her apartment with her children. Later that night, she left some food and water in her children's room, opened their bedroom window, then affixed a slip of paper consisting of only four words, "Please call Dr. Horder" on the baby carriage and concealed the gap around the kitchen door with towels. Turning on the gas of her kitchen stove, she placed her head as far as she could inside the oven, fell asleep from the carbon monoxide and took her own life.*

The Sylvia Plath example shows the phenomenon of coupling as it relates to suicide. Sylvia Plath constantly wrote about suicide and attempted it many times. People are not actively looking to kill themselves. Rather, they are looking for a way to kill themselves, and not just any method will do. Sylvia Plath had all of her conditions met at a vulnerable moment, and she died the way she wrote about in her poems. In the example of Sylvia Plath, the method of using "town gas" was right there in front of her and fit all her requirements: with the ultimate result being death, it was clean with no grotesque mess, and she could lie in an unchanged state. It was said Plath went out, "in a woman's way."

Even with thousands of deaths, including that of Sylvia Plath, authorities did not make the correlation between suicide and the "town gas." Governments never considered that town gas might lead to increased suicides. Rather, they stated that one of the positive side effects of transitioning to natural gas would be a decline in fatal accidents. There was no mention of suicide. However, if a person wanted to commit suicide now, they simply would find another means of doing so besides town gas. We call this displacement theory. So which theory was right? Displacement or coupling? If suicide follows the path of displacement theory and you blocked one method of suicide, people determined to commit suicide would simply succeed by other means, and the suicide rates would remain the same. If the coupling theory is correct, then suicide rates would decrease in line with the decreasing availability of a particular method. When an easy method such as "town gas" is made available, suicides typically rise. In the 1960s, the cost of "town gas" increased in Britain. Coincidentally, large reserves of natural gas were discovered in the North Sea, and the company British Gas converted all of Britain from "town gas" to natural gas. Natural gas differs from "town gas" because it has markedly different chemical properties and does not contain carbon monoxide. Every house, apartment, office, and factory had to be upgraded. It was one of the greatest peacetime operations in English history and took over ten years to complete. After 1977, if you put your head in an oven and turned on the gas, you would get little more than a headache. The overall number of suicides slowly decreased through the 1960s and 70s. By 1972, there were less than 100 suicides from gas asphyxiation, thus suggesting that the coupling theory was right. People are particular about how they take their own lives so removing their chosen method is a good strategy for prevention.

Catalytic converters mirror the "town gas" situation. Before catalytic converters, the amount of carbon monoxide released from a car's exhaust would quickly kill a person within 15 minutes. When catalytic converters became standard, car exhaust emitted negligible amounts of carbon monoxide and suicides by running cars inside a garage decreased accordingly.

What does the coupling theory tell us about suicides and the Golden Gate Bridge? The four-second fall from the Golden Gate Bridge sends a person at 75 miles per hour to hit the waters of the San Francisco Bay. Many die instantly from internal injuries, while others drown or die from hypothermia. Would it make a difference if a barrier on the Golden Gate Bridge prevented people from jumping? If the coupling theory is correct, then suicidal people would not seek out another bridge from which to jump from. Rather, the decision to commit suicide is coupled to a particular bridge.

According to Dr. John Mann, an expert in suicide, even in the most extreme cases, fear of death has a protective effect. When this fear inhibition is removed, and the person is no longer indecisive, suicide may occur. This is exactly what happens when a person decides to jump from the Golden Gate Bridge. Since the Golden Gate Bridge opened in 1937, there have been over 1700 suicides. It wasn't until 2018 that the authorities finally finished the suicide barrier, which in fact, was built to protect cyclists crossing the bridge rather than to prevent people from committing suicide. Again, it was assumed that if somebody wanted to commit suicide, they would do it. According to data released by the California Department of Public Health, 134 people under 18 died by suicide in 2020.

Certainly, using the coupling theory is not perfect when it is used to contextualize humans who are at risk of committing suicide. But the Sandra Bland case described in Gladwell's book shows the importance of coupling, and how it forms the larger picture for identifying the cause or trigger of a suicide. In the case of Sandra Bland, this trigger was from the "St. Louis Police stops." Trying to solve the overwhelming string of gun violence crimes, the St. Louis Police determined crime occurred in specific geographical regions and concentrated their patrols in those areas. They increased the number of traffic stops in those areas, and this resulted in a significant increase in arrests and the removal of weapons from the streets. These were known in the police community as "St. Louis style stops." These types of stops were then replicated across the country. Unfortunately, other police departments began implementing the same system, hoping for the same results. Instead of concentrating on areas of high crime, the police officers simply increased traffic stops, often for very minor offenses. Sandra Bland was pulled over in Texas for failing to signal a turn. The police officer pulled her over, the encounter escalated, which led to her being arrested and placed in a jail cell. Three days later, Sandra Bland committed suicide in her cell. She was in the correct state of mind, in the right place, and in the right environment to commit the act of taking her own life.

Suicide affects everyone, no matter their place in society. In terms of coupling, the COVID-19 crisis is providing all the elements needed for suicide to occur. Adolescents are placed in hopeless and overbearing environments, with access to firearms in the home and tutorials on constructing a noose and other forms of suicide on their school-issued iPads. Combine all this with feelings of isolation and the inability to see friends or family, a person, child, or adolescent might see suicide as a viable option.

# CHAPTER SEVEN:
## TRADITIONAL TREATMENT OF DEPRESSION AND SUICIDE - AND KETAMINE

*"A sad soul can kill you quicker than a germ."*
—John Steinbeck

Major depression is the leading cause of disability worldwide. The COVID-19 crisis has already magnified the problem in people with mental-health disorders. Sixteen million adults experience an episode of major depression each year. Antidepressants, electro-convulsive therapy (ECT), psychotherapy, cognitive behavior therapy, lithium, and clozapine are standard treatments for depression and to prevent suicide. Each of these longstanding treatment modalities has an established efficacy for reducing markers of depression and suicide risk, but no chemical or physical treatment for depression has been entirely successful. Unfortunately, over 50 percent of patients will be resistant to any one approach. Pharmaceutical companies have not invested in medical research for new psychiatric medicines. With suicides at their highest number in 30 years, medical experts agree a rapid treatment for depression and suicide is highly desirable.

What if we had an intervention to stop suicide in its tracks and significantly drop the death rate? Well, there are such interventions and not enough people know about them - that is what this book is about. The longer a person is in a state of severe depression and expressing suicide behavior, the greater the risk of injury and death. Having a mental disorder, no matter what type (ADD, depression, bipolar, etc.), will on average, decrease a person's lifespan by one-third. Traditional treatments for depression and suicide take weeks or months to work, leaving a window of danger during which they may pursue suicidal acts.

# THE MONOAMINE HYPOTHESIS

The traditional treatment of mental disorders emanates from a 1950s hypothesis asserting that depression is caused by low levels of chemical messengers in the brain called monoamine neurotransmitters, which include serotonin, dopamine, and noradrenaline. The idea is to "increase" or "balance" the levels of these neurotransmitters in the brain and the depression will lift. Researchers accidentally discovered the monoamine hypothesis in the 1950s, when it was observed the popular medications for tuberculosis (isoniazid and iproniazid) resulted in patients becoming more cheerful, optimistic, and physically active, thus improving depression along with curing tuberculosis. Tuberculosis was the modern-day leprosy, and they placed those inflicted in sanatoriums which were essentially places to quarantine people from society, resulting in high rates of depression. People given these new tuberculosis drugs unexpectedly became happy and described having a "sunny mood." They perked up and even demanded activities from the administrators who did not know what to do nor why it was happening. Some became manic, which is a side effect of many antidepressants. They found isoniazid inhibited the enzyme called monoamine oxidase, which breaks down the monoamines: serotonin, norepinephrine, and dopamine. The discovery ushered in a new class of drugs called monoamine oxidase inhibitors, or MAOIs.

Several classes of antidepressant medications developed on the monoamine hypothesis fall into categories such as selective serotonin reuptake inhibitors (SSRIs), serotonin-norepinephrine reuptake inhibitors (SNRIs), tricyclic antidepressants (TCAs), and monoamine oxidase inhibitors (MAOIs). These categories of medications target one or more of the monoamine neurotransmitters and cause them to remain in the synaptic cleft which is the space between the neurons. Today, however, we know the monoamine theory does not reveal the complete picture. Medications alone often aren't enough.

Non-pharmaceutical treatments for depression such as cognitive-behavioral therapy (CBT), electrical convulsive therapy (ECT), trans-cranial magnetic stimulation (TMS), exercise, diet, and health optimization are used with antidepressant medications. Cognitive-behavioral therapy is a form of psychological treatment that has been effective for problems including depression, alcohol and drug use, suicide, and severe mental illness. It has been extensively studied in the management of suicide. Using the principles of Zen and contemplative practices, the primary aims of CBT are to strengthen problem-solving skills, ensuring that suicide is not the only choice for distressed individuals. In combination with pharmacological treatment, CBT involves highly structured components for each aspect of therapy, including group and individual skills training, individual therapy, and phone and video chat. Typically lasting for 10 to 20 sessions, some studies have shown CBT is helpful in treating those who have made prior suicide attempts, decreasing recurrences by up to 50 percent. Electrical convulsive therapy is regularly used to treat refractory depression (depression not responsive to treatment) and suicidal ideation. Under general anesthesia, doctors deliver electrical shocks to the head in a dose-dependent manner, resulting in brain seizure activity. Complications include bodily and dental injury, confusion, and amnesia. ECT sometimes produces a rapid response, but multiple treatments are required before achieving a therapeutic effect. Unfortunately, many deaths by suicide take place in the period immediately post-discharge after ECT, and doctors are unsure why. TMS involves a large magnetic coil placed on the head near a part of the brain believed to be important for mood. Magnetic pulses painlessly pass through the skull to stimulate brain cells and relieve depression.

Physical fitness and health optimization improve depression and suicidal behaviors. Both are protective and serve as methods of "self-treatment." Regular aerobic exercise, especially endurance exercise, has successfully helped many at risk of suicide. Exercise produces proteins like BDNF and stimulates other favorable biochemical changes in the brain. Many psychiatrists are now employing a whole food, lower-carbohydrate ketogenic diet as an adjunct to treat their patients with depression and other mental disorders.

Antidepressant medications have been the mainstay of psychiatrists treating mental disorders for over 50 years. The FDA has approved over 20 medications to treat psychiatric disorders, but more options do not always mean better outcomes. Antidepressants take weeks or months to ease depression symptoms; even worse, these drugs only work for about 50 percent of people. The longest study conducted on depression treatment, the STAR*D trial, showed that more than half of people treated with several antidepressant medications still had persistent symptoms.

Clearly, the monoamine hypothesis does not fully explain depression. Fifty years of narrowly focusing on monoamine neurotransmitters for treating depression caused scientists to miss other mechanisms causing mental disorders. For example, research has shown that serotonin only makes up 20 percent of the neurotransmitters in the brain. The other 80 percent are the neurotransmitters glutamate and GABA (gamma-amino-butyric acid). We now know GABA and glutamate play a significant role in suicide and depression. We can imagine glutamate and GABA as a "push-and-pull" response, sparking and stopping electrical brain activity. The glutamate-GABA relationship regulates most brain activity, including mood. The over-secretion of glutamate causes neurons to become less adaptable at communicating with other neurons. We call this "neuronal cross-talk," which is necessary for establishing new neural pathways and important for overcoming mental disorders. Antidepressant medications result in neuronal growth in different parts of the brain by increasing proteins and growth factors such as BDNF. This fact was ignored for many years by researchers. Depression treatments beyond the conventional medications that target monoamine neurotransmitters include ketamine and other psychedelics such as psilocybin. Lithium reduces suicidal behavior differently from antidepressants and has been associated with a significant reduction in suicide risk and suicide attempts in patients with bipolar or major depressive disorder. The American Psychiatric Association has even written guidelines about the use of lithium.

## KETAMINE, DEPRESSION, AND SUICIDE

"Ketamine is the most important breakthrough in antidepressant treatment in decades," said Thomas Insel, the former head of the National Institute of Mental Health. Technically not a psychedelic, ketamine is a dissociative anesthetic, along with drugs like nitrous oxide (aka laughing gas) and PCP (Phencyclidine, a mind-altering drug with a street name of Angel Dust). It is currently a class III scheduled drug (approved for hospital or medical settings). At high doses, ketamine is an ideal anesthetic. At low doses, it causes hypnotic states, altered perception of sight and sound, pain relief, and dissociative and hallucinatory effects in humans. Perhaps better known in the rave scene and veterinary anesthesia, ketamine is one of the most enigmatic findings in modern psychiatry research. A single sub-anesthetic dose of ketamine can reduce depression and suicidal ideation. Since many antidepressants require four to eight weeks to have an effect, and because it can take several trials of different antidepressants to find one that will work, ketamine could fill that time gap or even function as a single agent. Ketamine can be helpful for anyone who is suicidal or suffering from severe depression. Many studies have shown the beneficial effects of ketamine within hours, even after a single treatment. The effects on depression persist even when the ketamine has exited your system.

Ketamine differs from other psychiatric medications. It is a rapidly acting drug that could prevent suicidal behaviors and the associated extreme emotional pain. Indeed, a sub-anesthetic dose of ketamine has established utility in many medical situations such as pain management, suicide, and depression. Aside from case reports, there have been many randomized, double-blind, placebo-controlled studies involving large numbers of patients using reliable placebos. Overall, most studies have found significant antidepressant effects following ketamine administration. However, like antidepressants, not all patients respond. In those patients who do respond, ketamine infusion quickly results in antidepressant effects. Recent studies show anti-suicidal effects that are independent of the antidepressant response.

Depression causes abnormally high prefrontal cortex (PFC) activity. In one study, subjects were given a ketamine infusion and a specialized MRI (fMRI) machine imaged their brain activity. The people with depression showed more normal activity in the PFC after ketamine administration. At least temporarily, ketamine seems to help people become "unstuck" from abnormal patterns of brain activity associated with repetitive, negative thoughts. The study was repeated in patients with suicidal thoughts. Four hours after the ketamine infusion, the area of the PFC that was hyperactive calmed down, which correlated with people reporting fewer thoughts of suicide. In this sense, ketamine may be akin to using a "defibrillator on the brain," putting it back into normal rhythm. Early studies showed that in surgical patients under anesthesia who were given a ketamine infusion along with other anesthetic drugs like propofol and fentanyl, there were improvements in depression and postoperative pain. Since ketamine's discovery, there have been great efforts to disentangle its complex molecular mechanisms and find broader clinical applicability. The antidepressant mechanism of ketamine is unclear but may involve glutamate and blocking NMDA receptors. In fact, other SSRI medications such as fluoxetine and citalopram have also been shown to block NMDA receptors. Through the inhibition of NMDA receptors, ketamine allows new brain cell connections to take place. This is a process called synaptogenesis.

In 1998, researchers from the University of Cambridge used ketamine to successfully treat eating disorders like anorexia-nervosa and bulimia, which had gained international attention. In 2000, Yale University researchers pioneered the use of ketamine for severe depression. Dr. Berman showed that a single sub-anesthetic dose of ketamine facilitated improvements in mood and depression scores of depressed and schizophrenic patients. A compelling accumulation of data followed, showing a robust, and relatively sustained, antidepressant effect. They hypothesized ketamine could help in understanding the symptoms of schizophrenia because of its dissociative effects. Interestingly, research showed that ketamine triggers glutamate production, which prompts the brain to form new neural connections. This makes the brain more adaptable and able to create new pathways, helping patients to reinforce positive thoughts and behaviors. Recent studies show that ketamine encompasses a rapid suppression of suicidal ideation, which is unprecedented in psychiatric practice.

Ketamine is also effective for treatment-resistant depression (TRD). It is important to understand the difference between depression and TRD. Imagine battling symptoms of sadness, sleep disturbance, low energy, and thoughts of death or suicide lasting two or more weeks. This is the definition of depression. Now imagine being depressed and trying several medications and therapies - only to discover that none work. This is treatment-resistant depression. In 2005, Australian physicians showed that a sub-anesthetic dose of ketamine combined with CBT improved the symptoms of TRD. Some of these patients were on several medications and underwent ECT for several years with no real improvement.

In 2006, a large trial studying the effect of ketamine infusions on patients with TRD showed improvement of symptoms after a single treatment. Then another two trials in 2009 showed positive benefits in TRD patients. In 2010, ketamine was used in palliative medicine with beneficial effects.

Some studies even showed that the effects of ketamine infusions were lasting up to six months. In 2012, ketamine research showed a decrease in suicidal ideation in patients with bipolar disorder. Studies from Europe, America, Macao, Israel, Iran, China, and many other countries demonstrate ketamine is well tolerated in all ages and independent of the route (oral, intranasal, subcutaneous, intramuscular, or intravenous). It is important to point out that researchers working alone (and often poorly funded) performed many of the studies on ketamine; but research is ongoing, and many formulations and clinics have since arisen worldwide.

## SUICIDE TREATMENT IN THE 21ST CENTURY

Suicide is unique and unlike other maladies. Either treatment is successful, or it results in the individual's death. A variety of methods have been used to evaluate suicidal ideation. Because of its acute and violent nature, suicide is difficult to study because it is impossible to have a control group and validating a person's response during a suicide attempt is difficult at best. The prospect of saving lives via a rapid reduction in suicidality has substantial public-health benefits. Due to the high suicide rates and the known relationship between suicidal ideation and attempts leading to death, effective suicide interventions are a national priority. In 2012, the U.S. government created the National Strategy for Suicide Prevention; however, suicide rates continue to rise in many U.S. states and worldwide.

Considering the limitations in the clinical management of acute suicidal ideation, using ketamine to treat suicidality and depression has gained interest worldwide. The potential to avert suicide, preserve life, reduce patient suffering, and lower health care costs is enormous.

Most studies are done in academic settings, but many new studies are coming out of private practice. One of the largest real-world studies to date involved 235 cases where ketamine infusions eliminated suicidal ideation. Psychiatrist Dr. Calabrese showed that over 80 percent of patients with suicidal ideation could decrease or eliminate their suicidal ideation after serial ketamine infusions. Four weeks after the treatments, she found none of the patients had attempted suicide, visited the emergency room, or been hospitalized. Most patients in her study needed three or more infusions to put their depression and suicidal ideation into remission. All patients in her clinic were treated with ketamine and received therapy by a board-certified psychiatrist.

The National Institute of Health (NIH) studied the effect of a single treatment using ketamine on two groups: "wish to live" and "wish to die." They found a significant number of the "wish to die" group switched to "wish to live." Ketamine specifically affects the desire to attempt suicide, independent of depression. This suggests that in some respects, suicidal behavior might be distinct from depression.

A 2009 study was the first of its kind to publish ketamine's effects on suicidality in 26 patients in a psychiatric hospital setting. Twenty-four hours after a single ketamine infusion, they observed large reductions in suicidal ideation. These researchers also saw a 50 percent decrease in overall Montgomery-Asberg Depression Rating Scale (MADRS) scores in those patients who received additional ketamine infusions. A 2013 study found that ketamine reduced depression 24 hours after treatment in 64 percent of patients who had tried three or more other medications with unsuccessful results.

In 2017, researcher Lucinda Grande described the use of oral ketamine to reduce suicidal behavior in two patients with a major depressive disorder. Ketamine was added to their treatment regime, and they were monitored closely. Both were given sublingual ketamine with instructions to take repeated doses every 1-2 hours until settled. The first man, aged in his sixties, described an increasing "sense of calm" after his second dose. Half an hour later he was markedly improved, smiling and joking. He was closely monitored by phone and clinic visits over the next month. He returned to work a week later and discontinued ketamine after a month. The second patient was a man diagnosed with bipolar disorder and depression. He had a history of attempted suicide. Grande prescribed him a daily dose of ketamine over six months. The patient said it was helpful in reducing suicidal thoughts together with increased support. Although this was a small study, it strongly suggested that repeated and relatively low doses of oral ketamine can rapidly reduce suicidal thinking.

Canadian researcher, Pierre Blier, carried out a series of studies on the effect of intravenous ketamine on suicidal ideation and major depression. In a 2016 trial, his team gave 19 patients seven ketamine infusions each. Over three weeks, 10 of the patients responded to the ketamine infusions with significantly lower depression scores, and just about everyone had lower suicidal ideation MADRS scores. Another study in 2016 described treating 27 patients, each receiving seven ketamine infusions. Of these, 16 patients had reduced depression and suicidal ideation scores. Those whose depression scores improved had a greater reduction in suicidal-ideation than the non-responders. In 2017, the group reported they had treated 34 patients of whom 50 percent had responded with lower depression scores and 90 percent had lower suicide ideation scores; once again, confirming a robust effect on suicidal ideation partly independent of reductions in depression.

Another researcher, Dr. Samuel Wilkinson, from the Yale Research Program, reviewed trials of intravenous ketamine in patients for whom suicidal thinking had been assessed. In this meta-analysis of 10 trials, there were 167 patients out of 298 who reported suicidal ideation at baseline. When patients were given a single intravenous ketamine infusion, they did better than the placebo group for up to seven days. Fifty-five percent of the ketamine-treated patients were free of suicidal ideation within 24 hours and reached up to 60 percent in just one week. Electro-convulsive therapy, by comparison, results in a 38 percent reduction in suicidal ideation after three or more treatments. In a 2018 review, Dr. Andrade concluded there is consistent evidence that a single dose of ketamine is associated with anti-suicidal benefits that can emerge within an hour of administration and persist for weeks.

In palliative care, ketamine presents a helpful and safe option. Patients with cancer have double the usual rate of suicide in the first two months of diagnosis. In 2016, Wei Fan published a study in which 42 patients with newly diagnosed cancer, depression, and suicidal thoughts were given a single intravenous dose of ketamine and saw significant improvement following the infusion.

### Esketamine - The First New Antidepressant in 20 Years

Janssen Pharmaceuticals recently brought to market the S-form of ketamine called esketamine, under the brand name Spravato. They developed esketamine because it is said to be more potent than regular ketamine, more patient-friendly, and increases the potential for more patients to receive the treatment. Racemic ketamine, which consists of equal parts of the S and R forms, is usually given via an intravenous infusion, which is invasive. Esketamine is given via nasal spray, which is easier to administer in an outpatient treatment setting under the supervision of a medical doctor. Esketamine has been effective when combined with an oral antidepressant such as Prozac. In one study, 70 percent of the patients with TRD improved on esketamine compared with the placebo. Following this powerful result, the FDA expedited the approval of esketamine for major depression. This is the first new drug approved for major depression in many years.

Clinical development of ketamine treatment faces many obstacles, primarily because its patent has expired and therefore, it receives limited attention from pharmaceutical companies. Combining other medications with a single dose of ketamine can have a significant effect on outcomes. Trials of esketamine reported rapid antidepressant effects in patients with treatment-resistant depression in conjunction with an oral antidepressant. One group was given intranasal esketamine twice weekly for four weeks together with other antidepressants. Post-administration, they showed reduced depression scores and a significant improvement in suicidal ideation scores after four hours with a numerical improvement after 24 hours. A third of the patients had a resolution of suicidal ideation 24 hours after the first dose of esketamine. Studies using Spravato for suicidal ideation are ongoing, and more studies are needed on esketamine. The jury is still out whether it is as strong as traditional ketamine infusions.

## KETAMINE ADMINISTRATION IN THE EMERGENCY DEPARTMENT

Emergency departments (ED) are regularly presented with patients having psychiatric medical problems including suicidal behavior, severe depression, bipolar disorder, mania, schizophrenia, and much more. In the U.S., 400,000 people are admitted to the emergency department for suicidal behavior each year and do not receive timely relief. The rapidity of ketamine's antidepressant effects has sparked interest in preventing and treating suicide in the emergency department and acute care settings. This makes ketamine an attractive candidate for securing the safety of patients who are at imminent risk of death by suicide.

In an interview with Dr. Thomas Insel, author of the new book *Healing: Our Path from Mental Illness to Mental Health*, Insel vocalizes his belief that the real benefit of using ketamine in suicidal patients will be in the ED. "By 2025, we will give ketamine to patients primarily in the emergency departments, and not in outpatient clinics," he says. The challenge for now is convincing insurance companies and hospitals to adopt new policies and cover the cost of ketamine administration. Dr. Insel explains as we become more adept at diagnosing who is most-at-risk to suicide, we will naturally move towards using a fast-acting medication like ketamine in emergency departments. It is disturbing that most people who kill themselves have, in some way or another, touched the mental-health care system but have not been targeted for prevention. Currently, we are poor at assessing risk and physicians do not know who, when, or how a suicidal patient will present.

"For now, we don't know how to assess risk or who is going to kill themselves in the next 24 hours," Dr. Insel says. Ketamine has been used in emergency departments for many years to sedate children and adults for procedures. So, for doctors in the ED to start using ketamine for mental-health emergencies such as suicidal ideation, ketamine will be an easy transition. In psychiatry, a suicidal patient in the emergency department is called a "warm hand-off." This is because the first month after discharge from an inpatient unit or the ED is the highest period for the risk of death. Ketamine could offer vital support during this vulnerable period.

The interest in ketamine to reduce suicidal ideation is gaining acceptance among emergency room physicians and other acute-care facilities. If a person responds to ketamine, suicidal ideation can be reduced rapidly, possibly avoiding hospital admission. Many studies have focused on using ketamine in an emergency-room setting, showing it is safe and a potentially effective treatment inducing the rapid remission of depression and acute suicidal ideation. In one study, ketamine was given to patients in the emergency department, and their symptoms diminished rapidly and significantly within 40 minutes, with no evidence of recurrence after a 10-day follow-up. Instead of requiring hospitalization, patients can be cared for in less-restrictive settings and maintain their usual support networks. Given that being in a hospital is not a barrier to suicide, we can also use ketamine in inpatient wards. By prescribing ketamine, doctors can create a bridge until more extensive help can be mobilized. Ketamine needs to be seen as a starting point for intensive treatment, not as an answer. Currently, ketamine is not routinely used in the emergency department for patients suffering from suicidal ideation or severe depression. Training the workforce is necessary and expensive but putting the pieces together will reduce risk and save lives. Imagine if Dr. Breen had been offered a medication like ketamine to suppress her suicidal ideation. Perhaps she would not have taken her own life. We will never know; but, based on the research, ketamine might have stopped her suicidal ideation in its tracks. It would have given her the precious time she needed to seek help. Further research is ongoing, and hopefully 21$^{st}$-century medicine will evolve, making ketamine available for anyone who needs it.

## POSTPARTUM DEPRESSION AND KETAMINE

Suicide is a leading cause of death among new mothers. Postpartum depression (PPD) and suicide are a silent health crisis. The COVID-19 related disruption in mental-health care is likely to lead to increased PPD and anxiety, resulting in maternal and child mortality. Postpartum suicide usually occurs around childbirth and at any time during the first year. It is estimated PPD occurs in approximately 10–20 percent of mothers, irrespective of culture or race. Postpartum depression severely impairs maternal quality of life, and accounts for 20 percent of postpartum deaths. We have no effective prophylactic treatment for PPD. While suicide is a leading cause of death in perinatal women, suicide during pregnancy or the postpartum period is under reported. A recent study found that suicide attempts during pregnancy, and after childbirth are increasing, nearly tripling over the past decade. Untreated mental-health conditions put both mothers and their children at higher risk for adverse health outcomes, including preterm birth and maternal suicide. In the U.S., nearly 24,000 mothers are at risk of suicide. Ketamine may have a role in treating PPD and possibly preventing suicide. It has been used for many decades as an anesthetic during difficult childbirths and cesarean sections. A study where ketamine was given during childbirth showed a significant improvement in postpartum psychiatric disorders and decreased antenatal depression and suicidal ideation. This study supported the idea ketamine can prevent postpartum psychiatric disorders. Ketamine affects the glutamate pathway and increases the levels of serotonin and melatonin, which contribute to the mother's well-being and antioxidant status. Taken together,

113

these findings suggest the increased PPD risk of antenatal depression, moderate stress, and suicidal ideation may be relieved by ketamine. An interesting side note is a new study from Columbia University linking general anesthesia to PPD. A body of research has shown that compared with regional anesthesia, general anesthesia is linked to increased risk for PPD after cesarean section. The authors of the report believe PPD results from the consequences of general anesthesia, where the patient is unconscious, which therefore delays the first skin-to-skin contact between the mother and child, delaying the first breastfeeding attempt.

## CHILDREN AND KETAMINE

Ketamine has been used for over 50 years in children for anesthesia and sedation; however, there is a paucity of research in using ketamine in pediatric depression and suicide. Does the question then become what is going to be better in the long-term? Suicide in children is on the rise, and real, as shown by many students who committed suicide in Las Vegas and elsewhere during the pandemic. There are problems with admitting children into the hospital because of the anxiety of being away from their parents. Treating children with ketamine for suicidal ideation may be a logical choice if it will provide time for the child and parents to get help. Ketamine is safe to use in children, but there is insufficient clinical data on how sub-anesthetic doses of ketamine for depression affect the developing brain. Ongoing studies have found ketamine can lower symptoms in severely depressed teenagers.

## KETAMINE ASSISTED PSYCHOTHERAPY

The psychiatric establishment has taken advantage of ketamine's psychedelic effects. Ketamine assisted psychotherapy uses a dosage escalation strategy to achieve different mental states, ranging from euphoria to full out-of-body experiences. Ketamine assisted psychotherapy has become more popular especially during the COVID-19 crisis. It also coincides with recent clinical research with psilocybin assisted therapy, which is currently in phase 3 FDA trials. Currently, ketamine is the only legally available psychedelic medication for assisted psychotherapy.

Dr. Phil Wolfson is the president of the Ketamine Research Foundation and specializes in ketamine-assisted psychotherapy. He and his colleagues have created online sharing groups. Dr. Wolfson attests that no one comes back the same from a ketamine treatment. Patients often report feeling like they are part of the cosmos, experiencing different colors and light, and can feel more connected with their environment in ways not otherwise possible. Dr. Wolfson published a paper in 2019 where a significant portion of the patients were over 65 years old. He has treated many geriatric patients without difficulties. Dr. Wolfson is 77-years-old and uses ketamine on himself with no untoward effects. His oldest patient is 87-years-old and has done very well with ketamine infusions. Even patients with transient increases in blood pressure and heart rate could tolerate ketamine treatments.

The effectiveness of ketamine assisted psychotherapy lies in several factors. Depending on the dose, ketamine promotes a timeout of sorts from ordinary thoughts, a relief from negative emotions, and an openness to expanding the mind with access to "the self." These effects enhance the patient's ability to engage in meaningful psychotherapy during and after administration. It is potent for recovery from depression and the lingering effects of trauma. One or two sessions are necessary to find the optimal amount of ketamine for an individual. The sessions are intensive, fatiguing, and can last for up to three hours, but ketamine-assisted psychotherapy is rewarding for its practitioners and their patients.

Ketamine-assisted psychotherapy has been used for over 50 years in the treatment of heroin, cocaine, and alcohol dependence, as well as food addiction. After alcohol detoxification, ketamine showed over a 60 percent success rate in keeping patients abstinent from alcohol. Thousands of patients have been detoxified from alcohol using ketamine with no reported complications. Three stages define ketamine assisted psychotherapy: the first stage is preparatory, during which patients undergo a preliminary psychotherapy session in which they are directed to view the world symbolically, realize the negative effects of alcohol dependence, and see the positive sides of sobriety. In the second stage, ketamine is administered intramuscularly, and the psychotherapist verbally guides the patient to create new meaning and purpose in life. At moments of a highly intense psychedelic experience, the smell of alcohol is introduced to the patients. In the third stage, psychotherapy is performed after the session. With the help of a therapist, patients share their experiences with others the following day after the ketamine session.

## KETAMINE AND PTSD

Considering the often crippling psychological weight of these factors, we return our focus to the importance of ketamine. A VA-funded study evaluated the safety and efficacy of repeated doses of ketamine to reduce PTSD symptoms in both active military personnel and veterans, with much success. The military has traditionally used ketamine for anesthesia in war zones; thus, it is not surprising to see an interest in its efficacy to treat PTSD. Ketamine given to soldiers during surgery for burns sustained in Afghanistan and Iraq had the unexpected benefit of reducing the incidence of PTSD by 50 percent compared to those who were treated with other anesthetics. The Army has supported further research into the treatment of PTSD.

In 2014, Feder and Charney showed that ketamine could be helpful in the short term to treat PTSD. They conducted a study of 41 non-medicated patients diagnosed with PTSD. It was a randomized, double-blind, placebo-controlled trial with a crossover period of two weeks. They focused on the 24-hour post-infusion response, and it showed a significant improvement for the ketamine group compared to the control group. This improvement persisted for many of the soldiers. Patients with co-morbid depressive symptoms also improved, but this did not influence ketamine's effect on PTSD. Side effects such as feelings of dissociation were mild and transient. The authors concluded that the results of the trial required replication and extension of the use of multiple doses of ketamine. They also speculated using ketamine for anesthesia and pain relief for traumatic injury should be further explored as a way of preventing PTSD in these patients.

A further trial published in 2018 by Basant showed that combined-mindfulness psychotherapy and ketamine are effective in treating PTSD. A 20-patient study examined the length of sustained response with combined "Trauma Interventions using Mindfulness-Based Extinction and Reconsolidation" (TIMBER) and ketamine. Clearly, more research needs to be done using ketamine for PTSD conditions, but the initial results are promising.

## CHRONIC NEUROPATHIC PAIN AND KETAMINE

Neuropathic pain is difficult to treat and requires multiple medications, including narcotics. Ketamine allows the patient to remember what it was like to be pain free. It is a potent adjunct medication for treating pain as it decreases the need for taking opioid medications; this is useful in chronic pain treatment. We often associate refractory depression with chronic neuropathic pain. Increasingly ketamine has been used in both children and adults to treat chronic refractory pain, especially with severe depression. There is even research showing ketamine can help treat "phantom limb" pain that is experienced after the amputation of a limb.

### Case: Nurse Practitioner with Neuropathic Pain

*This nurse practitioner had a chronic pain condition called trigeminal neuralgia, resulting from a viral infection. Trigeminal neuralgia is a painful condition in the face because it continuously stimulates the facial nerves. He tried standard therapy for years, including anticonvulsants, physical therapy, and antidepressants. Being on his medications caused him to become disabled, and he was no longer able to work. His disability caused him to have major depression, which eventually became paralyzing. After years of pain, disability and suffering, his neurologist suggested a lidocaine infusion which helped intermittently. He was then offered a ketamine infusion for 48 hours in the hospital. He described it as a transformative experience and remarked it was the first time in over six years that he could remember what it was like not to feel pain. The ketamine infusion also lifted his depression. With further treatment, he returned to work and lived his life normally, even though he was not 100 percent cured.*

*Source: Shrink Rap Radio Podcast #725. www.shrinkrapradio.com*

The mechanism of neuropathic pain differs from other types of pain. Ketamine blocks the N-Methyl D-Aspartate (NMDA) receptors involved with neuropathic pain. Since ketamine regulates NMDA receptors, we believe it influences the opiate system as well. In addition, NMDA receptors are involved in the development of opioid tolerance. The role of the opioid system has recently caught the attention of the scientific community, partly because increased suicide rates are linked to the current opioid crisis. The opioid system takes part in pain processing, and its involvement in ketamine analgesia has been shown in animal and genetic studies. Adverse experiences, such as childhood abuse, have resulted in epigenetic changes in the opioid system. It is well known the opioid system is involved in reward, pleasure-seeking, and decision-making systems. These systems are highly impaired in suicidal behavior.

It is interesting that naltrexone, an opioid receptor partial agonist, has been associated with a decrease in suicidal ideation. Recently, a study was done where TRD patients received naltrexone and ketamine. The results showed that ketamine with the addition of naltrexone, profoundly attenuated the antidepressant effect. It has been proposed that ketamine alters conscious pain perception. Human studies have shown that a single sub-anesthetic dose of ketamine selectively improves the effective component of pain. These findings are relevant, as suicidality is strongly associated with both physical and psychological pain. Actor and comedian, Robin Williams committed suicide because of psychological pain.

## A Brief Review of Ketamine Pharmacology

Ketamine belongs to the chemical class of drugs known as the arylcyclohexylamines. In 1962, Professor Calvin Steven created a derivative of phencyclidine (PCP) called CI-581 through animal studies. The first human administration was in 1964, and they found it to produce dissociative anesthesia. The FDA approved ketamine for surgical anesthesia in 1970. Ketamine does not overly suppress breathing or blood pressure, which increased its popularity. It is often the only anesthetic in developing countries. In fact, the WHO labels it as an essential medicine, because one can administer it without supplemental oxygen or a supply of electricity, which are necessary for the administration of many other anesthetics. Used as a "buddy drug" for injured soldiers, ketamine gained widespread use in the Vietnam War, because it could be administered by a fellow soldier due to its relative safety. The U.S. military still uses it today in the Middle East conflicts.

Ketamine is a mainstay for anesthesia and analgesia in veterinary medicine. It is the only injectable anesthetic that is effective in a wide range of species. In the 1970s, ketamine hit the streets and was known by names like "Special K" and "Vitamin K." People who used ketamine and other psychedelics like LSD were known as "psychonauts." In the 1990s, ketamine abuse was evident, and there were efforts worldwide to limit illicit use. Lawmakers relabeled ketamine as a schedule-3 non-narcotic substance under the U.S. Controlled Substances Act. This further decreased studies of ketamine and psychiatric disorders. Ketamine's patent expired in 2002, so pharmaceutical companies had little incentive to study the drug.

Ketamine exists in two forms: the S (+) and the R (-) configurations. These are called enantiomers and exist as mirror images of each other. The S form is approximately twice as powerful as the R form. Distinguishing the different effects between the two forms is difficult. Current pharmacological preparations of ketamine comprise equal proportions of the two forms which is called a racemic mixture. The bioavailability of intramuscular (IM) ketamine is comparable to intravenous ketamine. Oral or sublingual administration of ketamine is variable, but some sources estimate its absorption is 15 to 25 percent. A summary of the bioavailability is as follows: intravenous (100%), intramuscular (93%), nasal (25-50%), oral (17-24%), and sublingual (24-30%). The half-life of ketamine is one to three hours, meaning that half of the drug is eliminated from the body in this time. The subjective effects (euphoria, dissociation) cease quickly after the administration is stopped. In the liver, it is metabolized into four distinct metabolites (hydroxynorketamine, dehydronorketamine, hydroxyketamine, and norketamine).

The specific stages of ketamine-altered states of consciousness exist as a function of drug dose. A low, sub-psychedelic dose (25 to 50 mg IM injection) results in an empathogenic experience: one characterized by happiness and an increased awareness of the body. With a medium psychedelic dose, (50 mg to 125 mg IM injection), people have out-of-body experiences, meaning that subjects feel a complete separation from their body. Finally, in a high dose (150 to 200 mg IM injection), subjects undergo an ego-dissolving transcendental experience. In this state, individuals feel a dissolution of boundaries between the external reality and self and can have a "near-death" experience.

## The Food-Mood Connection. How diet and Metabolic Health Can Treat Depression and Suicide

We know diet and nutrition play an important role in mental-health. The reason it makes sense to look at your diet is because the most powerful way to change your brain chemistry is through food. Food is where brain neurotransmitters like glutamate come from in the first place. We need a diet that includes all the nutrients the human brain needs; and one that supports the brain's energy over a human lifespan. Also, our diets must exclude all the things that damage the brain, such as vegetable oils and processed sugars. All mental diseases involve brain inflammation, oxidative stress, nutrient deficiencies, and insulin resistance. Dr. Chris Palmer is a Harvard Psychiatrist dedicated to improving the lives of people suffering from mental illness. His research is focused on how we can improve mental-health disorders by understanding diet and metabolism. Dr. Palmer is pioneering the use of the ketogenic diet as a treatment for psychiatric disorders. We have used the ketogenic diet for over 100 years in the treatment of epilepsy. Recent research published in JAMA Psychiatry suggests that insulin and obesity, two factors closely linked with diet, may be powerful predictors of children developing serious mental illness. They studied over 15,000 children ages 1 to 24 and measured fasting insulin levels and body mass index. Children who had persistently high insulin levels, a sign of carbohydrate intolerance, were five times more likely to be at risk for psychosis. They were also more likely to develop depression. This finding was not statistically significant, but nonetheless, it was a very important finding. Depression is the leading cause of disability both in the U.S. and worldwide. By addressing insulin resistance (carbohydrate intolerance), there is evidence switching to a low carbohydrate and/or non-processed diet, such as a ketogenic or Mediterranean diet, may help depression. With the prevalence of obesity and diabetes in the U.S. (currently at over 100 million people), this becomes very important. Patients with diabetes are three times more likely to struggle with depression. Keeping insulin low through our diet and lifestyle has tremendous effects on our brains. Using these types of diet interventions will produce mood stabilization and optimize energy function within the brain. A ketogenic diet, which causes the body to preferably use fats for energy, can stabilize glutamate levels in the brain, which are associated with depression and suicide. While there is not yet enough research to recommend a low-carbohydrate or ketogenic diet as a standard treatment of psychiatric disorders, the research is promising, and there are no medications or prescriptions required to try this approach.

# CHAPTER EIGHT:
## NEUROLOGICAL BASIS OF HOW KETAMINE STOPS SUICIDE

*"We are always looking for simple answers to complex problems, and they are nearly always wrong."*
—H.L. Menken

Ketamine has been in clinical use for over half a century, yet its precise mechanisms remain a mystery. How ketamine works against suicide and depression is not entirely clear. We know the biochemical processes involved in depression go well beyond the monoamine hypothesis, and that ketamine works as a psychedelic, hypnotic, analgesic, and antidepressant. Ketamine affects a host of cellular functions including genes, neurotransmitters, hormones, cytokines, and receptors. These effects may be due to increasing glutamate levels, decreasing brain inflammatory molecules, and activating proteins like BDNF and mTOR. Ketamine increases glutamate in the brain by blocking the NMDA receptor. Ketamine increases the communication among existing neurons by creating new connections and enhancing brain circuit activity. Recent research has revealed that ketamine administration in rats and monkeys leads to increased growth and function in dendritic spine synapses in the prefrontal cortex.

Ketamine is a pharmacological agent that induces neuroplasticity. The term neuroplasticity was coined in the 1900s. Prior to the 1900s, the adult brain was thought to be a nonrenewable organ, meaning once your brain cells are formed in adulthood, they are finite and cannot be changed or grow back. We now know this not to be true. One leading theory suggests medications like ketamine stimulate the growth of connections between neurons (i.e., neuroplasticity). There are billions of pathways in our brains resembling roads. Some of these roads are more traveled than others. For example, our habits are well established neural pathways; but as we do new things, we create new pathways in our brains. This is the essence of neuroplasticity. Ketamine increases the functional connectivity in brain circuits, which helps explain its rapid antidepressive effects.

Scientists always knew children's brains were constantly growing and changing. At birth, an infant's brain has around 7,500 neuronal connections, and this doubles by two years of age. Today, we know that new brain cells and pathways are formed even into old age. We already use medications and chemicals to change the way our brain works, and psychology has shown our thought patterns can cause significant changes to our brain structure and function. Enhancing neuroplasticity in adults can result from new environments, focused cognitive training, physical activity, fasting, restorative sleep, and psychoactive agents such as ketamine and psilocybin. Both pre-clinical and clinical studies show that ketamine reconfigures disrupted prefrontal connectivity, restoring normal metabolic homeostasis. Changes in brain circuits take place in many parts of the brain, including the anterior cingulate cortex, prefrontal cortex, and hippocampus. Abnormalities in these areas, especially the prefrontal cortex and cingulate cortex, have been consistently reported in patients with a history of suicidal ideation. Therefore, ketamine's anti-suicidal action might be related to its ability to restore impaired brain connectivity through neuroplasticity.

Measuring the strength of connections between different brain areas affected by depression is a recent phenomenon. This is important because the increase in neuronal conductivity is thought to relieve depression. Traditional antidepressants focus on two neurotransmitters in the brain: serotonin and noradrenaline. An imbalance in the levels of these two neurotransmitters were thought to cause depression, and that antidepressants restored the balance of these chemicals. However, it was recently found that these chemical changes in the brain occurred quickly after taking antidepressants. It was then surmised antidepressants likely work by increasing the number of new nerve cells and pathways formed in certain areas of the brain. Psychotherapy, exercise and ECT are also thought to work in this manner.

Ketamine changes the balance between the neurotransmitters glutamate and GABA. Alcohol, for example, inhibits both of these neurotransmitters. Glutamate is essential for normal brain functioning, and its levels must be tightly regulated. It is an excitatory messenger and is the workhorse for the brain. It turns on neurons, triggering an electrical impulse. Glutamate is the reason you can still ride a bike years after you first learned. Eighty percent of large cells in the higher brain release glutamate as their neurotransmitter. Smaller brain cells balance glutamate by releasing the inhibitory neurotransmitter GABA, which quiets brain activity. These excitatory and inhibitory molecules are among the most common and important in the brain. Abnormalities in glutamate function disrupt nerve health and communication, and, in extreme cases, may lead to nerve cell death. Abnormal levels of glutamate cause many negative symptoms including pain amplification, anxiety, restlessness, and even seizures. When ketamine binds to NMDA receptors, it increases the amount of glutamate and neuro-synaptic transmission, thus increasing neuroplasticity.

In the 1990s, through fMRI studies, researchers discovered ketamine causes a release of glutamate in the PFC and hippocampus, exciting numerous neurons. Glutamate then activates another receptor called the AMPK receptor. Together, the initial blockade of NMDA receptors and the activation of AMPK receptors cause the release of other molecules that help neurons communicate with each other via new pathways. This process likely affects mood, thought patterns, and cognition. Ketamine also has direct and/or indirect effects on many systems in the brain - the opioid, dopamine, serotonin, cannabinoid, nitric oxide, noradrenaline, sigma, GABA, and acetylcholine systems. These are all different brain messenger molecules. Over the years, several studies have corroborated the above results, refining and perfecting our knowledge or the intra-neural underpinnings of the antidepressant action of ketamine.

Depression is a disease of disconnection at many levels, including personal, social, and cellular. We associate depression and chronic insomnia with neuronal death and damage. Ketamine, through its action on the glutamate system, induces the quality and quantity of neuronal connections, thus improving the function of critical brain circuits. This allows people to deal more effectively with their problems after receiving medications like ketamine. Many pharmacologic treatments are currently in development that help recovery from depression and suicidal behaviors by encouraging neuroplasticity. Some of these include psilocybin, stem cells, changing gene expression, cellular proliferation, and regulating both inflammation and the immune system.

## BDNF, MTOR, AND KETAMINE

Healthy brain function depends on having the correct amount of BDNF in the right place and at the right time. Low levels of BDNF are found in animals and people with depression and suicidal behaviors. Decreased BDNF may predispose to neuronal degeneration, atrophy, and decreased dendritic numbers, leading to low synaptic activity and the clinical symptoms of depression. Brain tissue samples from suicide victims often contain abnormally low amounts of BDNF. People with severe COVID-19 infections also have low BDNF levels. BDNF is intimately involved in shaping neuronal synapses during brain development and throughout life.

Ketamine increases mTOR and BDNF through activation processes in the prefrontal cortex and hippocampus. Chronic stress is thought to result in a loss of BDNF producing brain cells, which leads to reversible structural changes manifested by a loss of connections and nerve cell atrophy. Increasing BDNF levels give rise to new neurons with the right connections, more branches, and more synapses. Intravenous administration of BDNF also has a rapid antidepressant effect in animals. Interestingly, in animal models of maternal deprivation, ketamine reverses depressive behaviors after a single dose. They also showed ketamine to protect the brain from oxidative-stress-induced brain damage by decreasing inflammation. Given ketamine's extensive effects on neuroplasticity in the regions mentioned above, and its normalizing effect on the hypothalamic-pituitary axis, ketamine may be useful in patients with a stress response of suicidal ideation.

Brain derived neurotrophic factor is a protein that is encoded by the BDNF gene. BDNF is a member of the neurotrophic family of growth factors, discovered in 1980 in swine brains. BDNF acts on specific neurons in the central nervous system and helps to support the survival of existing neurons, encouraging the growth and differentiation of new neurons and synapses. In the brain, it is active in areas vital to learning, memory, and higher thinking. BDNF itself is important for long-term memory. Proteins such as BDNF help stimulate and control brain plasticity. Mice born without the ability to make BDNF suffer developmental effects and die soon after birth, suggesting that BDNF plays an important role in normal neural development. BDNF initiates synapse formation through its effects on brain-receptor activity and supports the regular everyday signaling necessary for stable memory function. Physical exercise markedly increases BDNF in the human brain, a phenomenon which is partly responsible for exercise-induced neurogenesis and improvements in cognitive function. BDNF expression is significantly enhanced by the environment.

Many studies show links between decreased levels of BDNF in conditions such as depression, schizophrenia, obsessive-compulsive disorder, Alzheimer's disease, Huntington's disease, dementia, anorexia nervosa, and suicidal ideation. BDNF levels appear to be highly regulated throughout the lifetime, both in early development stages and in later stages of life. For example, BDNF appears to be critical for morphological development in certain structures of the brain, controlling behavioral processes like learning and motor-skills development. Studies of aging human brains have found that hippocampal volume decreases with decreasing plasma levels of BDNF, partially explaining the cognitive decline that occurs during aging. In addition, BDNF is a critical mediator of vulnerability to stress and stress-related disorders such as PTSD. Given the reduction in BDNF levels in people with various addictions, this seems a plausible mechanism for ketamine to have an anti-addictive effect.

The mTOR protein modulates several important social functions such as neuronal cell activity, metabolism, cell proliferation, death, and protein synthesis. Depressed patients have low activity of mTOR and decreased stimulation of neurons, causing depression. Ketamine rapidly activates the mTOR pathway in the prefrontal cortex, increasing intracellular protein synthesis and cell signaling. Many physiological processes such as memory formation and neuronal activity depend on mTOR.

## INFLAMMATION, SUICIDE, AND KETAMINE

Brain inflammation and suicide are strongly linked. Inflammatory molecules called cytokines, interleukins (IL) and tumor necrosis factor (TNF) are increased in suicidal patients, especially those with diabetes and obesity. These same inflammatory molecules are present in severe COVID-19 infections. The causal relationship connecting depression, suicide, and inflammation come from autopsy studies. For example, one study showed brain microglial activation consistent with inflammation in the autopsies of suicide victims. Another study showed increased levels of IL-6 in the cerebro-spinal fluid of suicidal patients. Inflammation leads to the production of molecules that bind to NMDA receptors. Ketamine specifically blocks these NMDA receptors. Although the mechanisms explaining the anti-suicidal effect of ketamine are unclear, current evidence points, in part, to the anti-inflammatory effect of ketamine. It has shown hippocampal upregulation of inflammatory markers such as IL, TNF, and kyeneurin can all be affected by the administration of a sub-anesthetic dose of ketamine.

COVID-19 is really two diseases: a severe viral infection and an immune system-mediated response syndrome. The SARS-CoV-2 virus appears to be extraordinarily adept at hyper-activating the patient's immune system. This is what is called a cytokine storm. The infection is described as having three stages. Eighty percent of those affected stay in stage 1 or 2A with a viral response and mild pulmonary effects. However, 20 percent of patients progress to stages 2B and 3, which have severe pulmonary effects and hyper-inflammation. The result is subsequent widespread inflammation throughout the patient's body, causing destruction to the tissues and rapidly leading to death. Early treatment of the immune-system dysfunction is critical. With the urgent need to develop new treatments for the COVID-19 infection, it is important to use everything available. Low-dose naltrexone is an opiate blocker and has been used to treat pain and inflammation in these disorders. Ketamine, given with naltrexone appears to reduce the production of tumor necrosis factors and interleukins. Ketamine and naltrexone have strong safety records in humans, are inexpensive, and are well tolerated. The ideal treatment for COVID-19 would be something that slows the progression of the disease to mild/moderate and prevents patients from becoming severe (stage 3). Ongoing studies are using intravenous ketamine and naltrexone to interrupt the severe inflammation secondary to COVID-19. The hypothesis is that ketamine and naltrexone act to change the immune-system response by reducing the severity of the cytokine storm. Traumatic brain injury also results in brain inflammation. Ketamine is a neuroprotective agent to prevent brain damage from head trauma, strokes, heart attacks, seizures, low oxygen levels (hypoxia), and low blood sugar (hypoglycemia) levels.

Our diet and lifestyles can also cause high levels of brain inflammation. Recent evidence suggests that adopting a non-processed food and low-carbohydrate diet can improve symptoms of depression, schizophrenia, and even suicide. Excess consumption of processed carbohydrates and vegetable oils leads to chronic inflammation and excess glutamate in the brain. In Dr. Kate Shanahan's book, *Deep Nutrition*, she details the harmful effects of processed vegetable oils in the brain. It is arguable vegetable oils are not meant for human consumption. Excess sugars are responsible for increased inflammation in the modern age. For example, in the 1700s, a human consumed about four pounds of sugar annually. In the 1800s, this increased to over 20 pounds. In the 1900s and into the industrial age, our level of sugar consumption has skyrocketed to over 100 pounds per year. Consider the fact the human body maintains blood sugar levels equivalent to 1 to 2 teaspoons of sugar (75mg/dl or 4mmol). When constantly exposing our bodies to sugar, the body reacts by producing inflammatory factors. Years of chronic sugar exposure causes our bodies to become intolerant to sugar or carbohydrates. The body's response to this excess sugar in the blood is energy storage. In humans, energy is stored in fat cells and causes deregulated energy production and inflammation leading to brain fog. This is the common link between human obesity and inflammation.

## The Detailed Mechanism of How Ketamine Binds to Receptors

Ketamine binds to receptors in the cell lipid bilayer. These receptors are called "PCP" receptors for historical reasons. Just imagine these receptors are tunnels with a portion sticking into the cell and a portion sticking out of the cell. When ketamine binds to these receptors, it causes a blockage. The outer end of the tunnel is attached to a glutamate receptor, which is called an NMDA receptor on the cell surface. The whole receptor complex is known as an NMDA – PCP or N–P receptor. The "N" part is on the outside and locks onto glutamate, and the "P" part is on the inside and locks onto ketamine. There are also binding sites for other chemicals, such as magnesium, which block the same tunnel. The complex is like a large space station with several docking bays for different spaceships.

It was once thought the P receptors are the same as PCP receptors, but now we know they are completely distinct entities. The N-P receptor complex plays an important role in thinking, memory, emotion, language, sensation, and perception. Ketamine has effects in all of these areas, changing how incoming data is integrated.

## Useful Terms and Definitions

Before delving into how ketamine works, it is useful to describe some of the terms involved.

**Neuron** - A brain cell. Neurons consist of a cell body (soma), dendrites, and an axon. The cell body contains a nucleus and receives incoming electrical nerve impulses through dendrites and the axon, which are an extension of the neuron.

**Synapse** - A specialized structure that permits a neuron to pass an electrical or chemical signal to another neuron or other cell. The synapse is where all the action happens. Neurons release chemical neurotransmitters that diffuse across a small gap and activate special sites called receptors. Ketamine effects opioid, serotonin, cholinergic, and catecholamine receptors.

**Neurotransmitters** - The chemical messengers that transmit signals across a synapse from one neuron to another. Neurotransmitters are chemical substances made by the neuron specifically to transmit a message. Examples of neurotransmitters are glutamate, norepinephrine, epinephrine, serotonin, and many others.

**Glutamate** -The major excitatory neurotransmitter used by all living things and thought to be the most important in the brain. Over 80 percent of neurons are said to have glutamate receptors and play important roles in cognitive functions, learning, and memory. One of the major actions of ketamine is to decrease or balance the action of glutamate.

**GABA** (Gamma-amino-butyric-acid) - is the chief inhibitory neurotransmitter in the brain. Its principal role is to reduce neuronal excitability. GABA is the opposite of glutamate in this sense.

**NMDA receptor** - NMDA stands for N-Methyl-D-aspartate. It is the glutamate receptor found in neurons and it is activated when glutamate and glycine bind to it. This results in a positive flow of electrically charged signals through the cells. The activity of the NMDA receptor is affected by many psychoactive drugs. Ketamine blocks the NMDA receptors.

**mTOR** - The mechanistic target of rapamycin (mTOR). A protein made by cells that acts as a signaling pathway. It serves as a regulator of cell metabolism, growth, proliferation, and survival. Ketamine activates mTOR signaling in the brain.

**BDNF** - Brain Derived Neural Growth Factor (BDNF). Found in the brain and spinal cord, this protein promotes the survival of neurons by playing a role in the growth, maturation, and maintenance of brain cells. In the brain, BDNF is responsible for plasticity, which is crucial for learning and memory. BDNF is increased by ketamine administration and certain types of exercise.

**Epigenetic** - This refers to heritable external modifications to phenotype that do not change the DNA. Epigenetics are the reason a skin cell looks different from a brain cell. Epigenetic changes are said to come from the environment and may play a role in suicidality, meaning a suicidal parent may pass genes to their children that may predispose them to suicide themselves. An example could be the offspring of a person produces less BDNF than normal people; thus, may have a predisposition to depression and suicide.

**Hippocampus** - Named for its shape (from the Greek for "sea horse"), this structure is a major component of the brains of humans and other animals. The hippocampus is part of the limbic system and handles many bodily functions. In the center of the brain, the hippocampus is important in the storage of long-term memories, response inhibition, and spatial cognition.

**Prefrontal Cortex** (PFC) - This region of the brain covers the front part of the frontal lobe and is responsible for planning, personality expression, decision-making, and moderating social behavior. It is linked to a person's will to live, short-term memory, personality expression, and certain aspects of speech and language. It is not fully mature until about 25 years of age in humans.

**Electro-convulsive therapy** (ECT) - A medical procedure performed under anesthesia, where small electric currents are intentionally passed through the brain, triggering brief seizures. ECT is said to cause changes in brain chemistry, quickly reversing symptoms of certain medical health conditions. For an in-depth story about ECT, you can watch the TED Talk by Sherwin Nuland - (https://www.ted.com/talks/

sherwin_nuland_how_electroshock_therapy_changed_me)

**Neuroplasticity** - also known as brain plasticity. It is the ability of the brain to change through growth and reorganization, form new connections and pathways and change how its circuits are wired. Once thought only to manifest during childhood, it is now known adult brains demonstrate neuroplasticity. The adult brain is not entirely hard-wired, and new brain cells are formed even in adulthood.

**Neurogenesis** - The ability of the brain to grow new neurons or brain cells.

### A Technical Explanation of Ketamine and Neuroplasticity

Researchers believe ketamine increases brain synapses by increasing the proteins BDNF and mTOR. Both molecules rev up the synthesis of biomolecules. Some of these biomolecules include lipids, proteins, and nucleotides. A more technical explanation of the mechanism of ketamine is in the interneurons in the prefrontal cortex, resulting in a surge of glutamate from the pyramidal neurons. Glutamate activates postsynaptic alpha-amino-3-hydroxy-5-methyl-4-isoxazolepropionic acid receptors, which trigger the well-known, mTOR-dependent protein synthesis and BDNF structural plasticity in the prefrontal cortex and hippocampus. A second hypothesis claims ketamine directly inhibits postsynaptic NMDA receptors on pyramidal neurons, which elicits the spontaneous release of glutamate, preventing the phosphorylation of eukaryotic elongation-factor-2, and resulting in rapid BDNF production. Animal studies show ketamine itself might target neural-plasticity independent of NMDA. These aforementioned theories converge on the activation of neuro-plasticity via the activation of BDNF and mTOR pathways. BDNF is a major brain growth factor activating intracellular signaling cascades; one of them being mTOR, which regulates synaptic protein synthesis. The rapid increase of mTOR in the medial prefrontal cortex following ketamine administration results in local structural plasticity.

# PART THREE:
# THE FUTURE

# CHAPTER NINE:
## KETAMINE SAFETY, PATIENT EXPERIENCE, AND NEAR-DEATH EXPERIENCES

*"Real science can be far stranger than science fiction and much more satisfying."*
—Stephen Hawking

## THE KETAMINE PATIENT EXPERIENCE

Ketamine is the one medication where it is legal and acceptable to go to a doctor and be prescribed a psychedelic experience. The goals are to reopen the sensitivity and sensibility of the individual along with reinstating their humanity and vulnerability to the world. We all carry an emotional armor that restricts expression and the love a person can give to themselves and others. With ketamine, the habitual defenses are removed as consciousness is dissociated from the body.

## WHAT'S IT LIKE ON KETAMINE?

Most report the experience of ketamine to be pleasant describing:
*"Ketamine filled in my missing piece."*
*"I feel whole for the first time since the accident 33 years ago."*
*"The world was brighter."*
*"A Christmas miracle."*
*"I was finally standing up straight and experiencing the world."*
*"It was like it melted my armor (of depression)."*
*"It was like I was in a biological membrane... very pleasurable."*

It is important to establish that ketamine is a medication that acts on the brain. The experience of ketamine happens in the mind. Some patients describe the sensory effects of ketamine as including a visible, buzzing, vibrating field around physical objects. Some describe the melting of boundaries of those objects. There may be magnification, diminution, or alteration of color intensity and hue. Colors sometimes generate auditory impressions, a blending of sense information called synesthesia. Psychedelics may allow users to see and experience things that others do not. In addition, what people may experience with their eyes closed may be superimposed on the outside world when they open their eyes. People often describe detailed geometric shapes, or enhanced details of a movement or picture. These "visions" can be extraordinarily complex and may comprise well-formed and recognizable objects like living creatures, machinery, and landscapes. Sound usually becomes softer or sometimes painfully harsh. Visualization of sounds, as well as unheard rhythms have been described. The effects on tactile and gravitational senses are pronounced. These range from dissociation of consciousness from the body to an extreme hypersensitivity to both inner and outer physical stimuli. Emotional changes are quite striking. A sense of feeling safe is often experienced; however, it is possible to feel uncomfortable or even terror.

Rapid fluctuation of emotion is often experienced between joy, anger, passion, hatred, shame, and grandiosity. Other times, a person may feel no emotions at all. Thinking may speed up or slow down. Many people experience new or philosophical insights, especially when the proper forethought and coaching takes place through therapy or meditation. Ketamine produces a sense of reality that may feel "more real than real" or like "a Cosmic Disneyland." Information arises from novel sources such as clouds, flowers, pictures, and objects. Psychedelics usually produce a state of increased suggestibility. Many describe an expanded sense of empathy to other people, animals, plants, and objects. Ketamine, when appropriately given, results in a peaceful experience, that gives the person a break from reality.

Hamilton Morris, a chemist who hosts the show, *Hamilton's Pharmacopeia*, describes ketamine as being similar to PCP but much shorter in duration, more of a psychedelic experience, and more sedating. Movement can be difficult, which makes it ironic that ketamine is often taken at dance-rave parties. With higher doses, you recede into yourself and enter a lucid, dream-like state. The imagery becomes increasingly abstract. Other psychedelics do not have the same sort of effects. Dissociative anesthetics tend to produce more random images.

The ketamine molecule does not contain a psychedelic experience per se; rather, it is your own consciousness that delivers the experience. Subjective descriptions of the ketamine experience include a sense of detachment from the body (dissociation), enhancement of insight into reality, a sense of relaxation or well-being. A sub-anesthetic dose of ketamine is a powerful psychedelic medication that makes it possible to have a conscious experience. It is a journey that lasts about an hour. Ketamine gives the person a break from reality, which is one reason it is helpful. Ketamine can have very different effects depending on your expectations and environmental setting. Desire to use ketamine to blow off steam and relax will result, in a different experience than it would for someone who is seeking to correct a mental illness.

The ketamine experience has some resemblance with the psychedelic plant, ayahuasca, in South America. People have profound psychological and philosophical experiences with ketamine, ayahuasca, and other psychedelic drugs. Many people go on to make profound life changes after a ketamine or ayahuasca experience such as disconnecting from dysfunctional relationships, changing from miserable jobs, kick-starting new careers, enrolling in higher education, and more. One difference between ketamine and ayahuasca is a person generally does not experience severe nausea and vomiting that is associated with the plant psychedelic.

Ketamine filters reality so that one gains an enhanced appreciation for the world, outside of categorical everyday kind of knowledge. With psychedelics, patients have subjective experiences where they feel they have gained new insights into their understanding of reality, as though a curtain has been lifted or a wall removed. This feeling is not a sort of inebriation or intoxication. After being under the influence of ketamine, the world does not appear to fit into verbal labels and categories. Everything seems connected and not linear.

To put this in perspective, imagine that our brains resemble a communist country like North Korea, which is governed by an authoritarian regime that tries to make sure nobody learns about the outside world through the internet. Our brains are similar in the way it allows information to enter and leave. Normally, our brains filter out certain thoughts and experiences that do not seem to fit our pattern or template of our quotidian experience. But when a person is experiencing ketamine, the brain realizes thoughts and information that are abstract from reality, and normally out of reach to us. Consider the example: You may have an extreme fear of having a needle inserted into your vein. Even if you tell yourself, it is just a small needle and it will save your life, your brain will not accept this information, but instead will fixate on how the needle will hurt you. Once that information from that outside world slips in, our brains work quickly to eradicate that knowledge. Under the influence of a psychedelic like ketamine, our brains filter out reality (the fear of needles in this case), so we can experience a different type of reality in which we each separate our thoughts and try to advance our own personal goals. Often, the experience results in the person having less or even no fear of needles.

## THE SAFETY OF KETAMINE

Ketamine's tolerability and safety have been demonstrated for over 70 years. There are many reports of patients taking legitimate ketamine consistently for over 10 or 15 years without indications of tolerance, dependence, or addiction. An extensive body of evidence shows the safety of using ketamine in office anesthesia and analgesia, in emergency room settings, operating rooms and outpatient pain management clinics. Ketamine is used in small doses to treat depression. When used for general anesthesia, an anesthesiologist gives ketamine in upwards of 10 times the dose prescribed for depression. For most ketamine treatments, a medical professional should be present and prepared to handle any adverse medical situations.

The most common side effects are dizziness, dry mouth, coordination problems, nausea, and somnolence. Other reported experiences include euphoria, feelings of unreality, blurred vision, disorientation, anxiety, and hallucinations. Every one of these side effects is transient, meaning they quickly resolve.

A review of over 70,000 published anesthesia cases highlights its safety. Studies from three different clinical trials of sub-anesthetic, intravenous ketamine administration for major depressive disorders found adverse effects including dizziness, self-actualization, and drowsiness. Whether these effects are considered benign or a part of ketamine's actual effects that resulted in therapeutic benefit is a subject of debate. About a third of patients experience mildly elevated heart rate and blood pressure. Some patients will develop symptoms of anxiety, which is from the dissociative side effects of ketamine. Often proper coaching and an appropriate environment minimize this risk.

Many people also report difficulty with balance, minor numbness, muscle weakness, and impaired vision after receiving ketamine. The drug's side effects can be predicted by the dose and route of administration. When the absorption of ketamine is rapid, as by the intravenous, intramuscular, or intranasal routes, the frequency and severity of side effects are greater. When ketamine is given orally, the side effects seem to be less. The treatment environment is important. A calm and positive environment is essential. It is not advisable to watch alien movies like "*Men in Black*" while experiencing ketamine.

A medical exam should always be performed prior to giving ketamine. The drug is rarely a problem in otherwise, healthy adults. However, ketamine can have different effects in small children and the elderly. Patients with cardiac problems such as high blood pressure or arrhythmia require monitoring. Ketamine can cause transient increases in blood pressure and heart rate. This is usually a good thing, as most anesthetics decrease heart rate and blood pressure. Mild heart palpitations may occur but are usually transient. Most anesthetics and sedatives will decrease breathing, ketamine has little effect on the respiratory system. Patients breathe normally while receiving ketamine, especially at the sub-anesthetic dose used in a ketamine clinic.

Patients having ketamine-related bladder problems called cystitis have been reported, including painful urination, decreased urine flow, and bloody urine. However, most of these have been addicts who often take street ketamine in daily doses over 3 to 10 grams. This is over 1,000 times the typical dose for intravenous ketamine used in a clinic. Furthermore, street ketamine often contains impurities pharmaceutical grade ketamine does not. Bladder problems like cystitis have not been reported as an outcome in any published trials of ketamine. Overall, ketamine has a very low rate of serious side effects. The multiple research trials of thousands of ketamine administrations given by physicians clearly show the potential benefits far outweigh the risks.

This story is from a chemistry doctor who speaks about the safety of ketamine as it relates to his depression:

### Case: Chemical Engineer - Anonymous

*We have shown ketamine as a potential treatment for depression for a very long time. I have benefited from ketamine infusions to treat chronic major depressive disorder. I credit the doctors for saving my life, but I get annoyed when "experts" complain about the side effects of ketamine. These side effects are far less damaging than the potentially terminal outcome of treatment resistant depression (TRD), or the impact of TRD on your life, job, and those around you. The potential for addiction to ketamine is always overstated. Infusions start at 0.5 mg/kg, way below the levels used by ketamine abusers and even the levels used by anesthesiologists who administer ketamine daily. I do, however, agree the long-term impact has yet to be evaluated, but I stand by my assertion, I'll deal with the complications in the future for a life now. Besides, ketamine infusions feel good, and there is plenty of anecdotal evidence that having an out-of-body experience suggests greater efficacy. The worst side effects I've experienced were nausea and vomiting, but Zofran (antiemetic) treats that when given prophylactically.*

*The saddest part of all this is ketamine costs just a few dollars and relieves major depression almost instantly. Unfortunately, insurers won't offer this treatment, as it is "off label," resulting in huge out-of-pocket costs. Part of the reason no company would fund the testing to approve ketamine for a new use is because there would be no patent protected profit. So it spurs some research and Janssen develops a patentable method to prepare a single enantiomer (hardly a simple process) and then gets approval for its use to treat depression when delivered intranasally. I am all for a company making money, but plain old ketamine works by infusion, IM injection, orally and nasally. However, Janssen's "rack rate" for esketamine is over twice the cost of the out-of-pocket ketamine infusion (approval trials and development are not cheap after all). Of course, insurance will pay a fraction of that, but I am guessing the total cost to the insurer plus your copay will still be significantly more than a ketamine infusion.*

## THE ADDICTION POTENTIAL AND SAFETY OF KETAMINE

Long-term recreational use of ketamine leads to tolerance, dependence, and addiction about 5 to 10 percent of the time. Ketamine bought on the street often contains other contaminants and substances, which can contribute to dependency. Ketamine given in hospitals and clinics is unadulterated and pharmaceutical grade. David Feifel studied 6,000 patient encounters describing just nine cases of addiction attributed to using ketamine in a clinic. Most of these patients had pre-existing addictions. Overdosing from ketamine is possible, as with any medication, however, if taken in a clinic or under physician supervision, all these risks are minimized.

## WHO SHOULD NOT USE KETAMINE?

There are very few absolute contraindications to trying ketamine, but there are certain groups who will require more intensive monitoring. Allergies to ketamine are extremely rare. A recent medical publication cited that 4 apparent allergic reactions have been reported over the past 50 years. In patients with cardiovascular instability, particularly uncontrolled high blood pressure, ketamine may be safer than alternatives but would require cautious dosing and a high level of supervision. Ketamine causes nausea in some patients, and a subset cannot tolerate the vomiting. A small percentage do not respond to ketamine, even at high intramuscular doses, especially those with rigid personality structures, severe obsessive-compulsive disorder, or other personality disorders. People who have difficulty entering a trance state often cannot sustain the benefits they experience from a session. People who have an active psychotic disorder (mania) generally should not be given ketamine. If they do, however, the patient should be thoroughly evaluated by a psychiatrist prior to the administration of the ketamine. People intoxicated with other substances should not be given ketamine.

In pregnancy, safety is not established. As of 2014, the FDA has not formally assigned ketamine to a pregnancy category. Animal studies at higher-than-human doses failed to reveal evidence of teratogenicity or impairment of fertility; however, there are no controlled data in human pregnancy. Since the safe use in pregnancy and delivery has not been established, the manufacturer recommends ketamine be contraindicated in pregnant women, even though it is regularly in obstetric anesthesia. The FDA has not classified ketamine under a pregnancy risk category. Australia's category B3: "Drugs which have been taken by only a few pregnant women and women of childbearing age, without an increase in the frequency of malformation or other direct or indirect harmful effects on the human fetus having been observed. Studies in animals have shown evidence of an increased occurrence of fetal damage, the significance of which is uncertain in humans." Ketamine breastfeeding warnings: "There is no data on the excretion of ketamine into human milk. However, because ketamine is a general anesthetic agent, breastfeeding would not be possible while using the drug. Ketamine should be undetectable in maternal plasma approximately 11 hours after a dose. Nursing after this time should not expose the infant to significant amounts of the drug." Closed-angle glaucoma: "There is a minor risk of increased intraocular pressure."

## WHO SHOULD USE KETAMINE?

There is a wide range of indications for the consideration of ketamine. Most commonly, ketamine is used for people with PTSD, severe depression, TRD, patients who have side effects from antidepressants, chronic pain syndromes, substance abuse disorders, OCD and eating disorders; self-enlightenment; and suicide prevention. An interesting indication for ketamine is called bipolar disorder with the fear of harm phenotype. This disorder rarely responds to traditional psychiatric drugs.

This story is from a creative director who speaks about how ketamine helped him with a rare type of bipolar disorder:

### Creative Director - James

James is a creative director and enjoys spending time with his wife and kids. However, it wasn't always like this. Despite having a happy childhood, he describes his thoughts as out of control. He describes an innate fear that is overwhelming, causing him to literally sleep with the cover over his head with just enough room to breathe through his mouth. James describes the fear akin *to crossing a busy freeway. His body temperature was always hot, sleeping with the windows open in the winter. James saw a doctor in his 20s who diagnosed him with ADD, so he started taking stimulants. He found himself putting things together and then taking them apart, feeling like he was in a massive downward spiral. He had always suffered from mood swings, but now they were becoming rapid and extreme, and his thoughts circled around gruesome scenarios. After finding himself unable to work, James sought help from Dr. Papolos in New York. He was diagnosed with a violent type of bipolar disorder called the fear of harm phenotype. This disorder rarely responds to traditional psychiatric drugs. So James started taking ketamine nasal spray every other day. His response was dramatic. He stopped overheating. On the first day, he turned to his wife and said he felt calm. James started working on his computer again and eventually returned to work a month later.*

Source: NPR - From Chaos to calm: a life changed by ketamine, 2018 https://www.npr.org/sections/health-shots/2018/06/04/615671405/from-chaos-to-calm-a-life-changed-by-ketamine

## THE MANY PATHS TO ENLIGHTENMENT-NEAR DEATH EXPERIENCES

Near-death experiences (NDEs) can be transformative in some people, inducing positive changes in spiritual development and worldview. Ketamine induced NDEs appear to be equivalent to natural NDEs. The psychology of NDEs may be an adaptive mechanism of the mind that alerts a person to the threat of death while the potential tidal wave of fear is kept at bay. This model may apply to situations like falling from a cliff and was originally developed from near-death experiences in mountain climbers. We know one part of the mind can split off or dissociate from another for psychological reasons. The purpose of this may be protection from anxiety so the ego can attend to unfinished business.

A sudden shock, such as being told a loved one has died, is often followed by an abrupt release of substances causing an increase in heart rate, shallow breathing, which creates "a knot" in the stomach. The substances include hormones such as noradrenaline and cortisol, which are released by ketamine. It is important to note that giving ketamine to individuals with damaged brain cells, such as those with Alzheimer's disease, does not enable them to recognize their loved ones or even remember their names. Ketamine may help them in other ways, but these are not obvious, and may be revealed in future research.

The mystical experiences and psychedelic effects of ketamine have not only been linked with positive outcomes in various treatments, but also those described as "life-changing" and "spiritually meaningful." The mystical experience of ketamine is important in its therapeutic mechanism. A sense of timelessness and eternity is also often experienced. Ketamine alters the default mode network, decreasing maladaptive, repetitive thoughts. The near-death experience (NDE) is an altered state of being that can be reached in various ways, including through drugs like DMT (dimethyltryptamine) and ketamine. We can reproduce all the features of a classical NDE in some people when ketamine is correctly administered. There are no agreed criteria defining the NDE. Some argue the difference between NDEs and a ketamine experience is that a true NDE can be unpleasant with no desire to repeat them. Important features include a sense that what is experienced feels real, and a sense that what is happening is inexpressible in words. Although there are often feelings of peace, joy, and euphoria, some cases have been frightening and unpleasant. The initial events may sometimes happen at high speed. Some describe being on a roller coaster, while many describe out-of-body experiences. Kenneth Rein, author of *Life and Death,* classifies the NDE 5-stage continuum: feelings of peace, detachment from the body, entering a transitional world of darkness (rapid movement through a long dark tunnel or "the total trip"), emerging into bright light, and entering the light. Ketamine allows some patients to reason the strange, unexpected intensity and unfamiliar dimension of their experience means they must have died. Near-death experiences may be therapeutic. The effects of an NDE can include an enhanced joy in living, reduced fear of death, increased concern for others, reduced levels of anxiety, reduced addiction, improved health, and resolution of various symptoms.

Ketamine has even been said to be neuro-protective, meaning it can prevent brain damage resulting from lack of oxygen or blood sugar, which may result from interruption of the blood supply during a heart attack or stroke. Interestingly, patients with severe oxygen deprivation during prolonged periods have had profound near-death experiences and, to the astonishment of the doctor's, sometimes survived the episode without impaired brain function. The lack of damage may result of blocking over-excitation, which is also how ketamine acts on the brain. Some people who have an NDE are less likely to suffer brain damage when the blood supply to the brain is impaired. Magnesium also blocks glutamate, which can protect cells from damage and stop seizures.

Interestingly, that sleep and dreaming involve the glutamate system. Interference with glutamate transmission has dramatic effects. A vivid example is the extensive loss of glutamate releasing cells in Alzheimer's disease and, to a lesser extent, in schizophrenia. Most large brain cells release glutamate, which also plays a key role in intelligence, memory, personality, and the features that make us human. Language, thinking ahead, making tools, and abstract thought are all known examples. Glutamate is also the primary messenger of sensation and perception. Ketamine affects all these areas.

Sean Spencer, a successful entrepreneur, launched a successful tech company in 2013. Looking from the outside, most would ask, "What does that guy have to be depressed about?" Unfortunately, it does not work like that. It does not matter if you have all the comforts of life: you can still be miserable. And in fact, entrepreneurs are twice as likely to suffer from depression. Sean's doctors prescribed him ketamine to treat his suicidal ideation. He underwent a series of ketamine infusions and was no longer suicidal.

Source: Wired magazine. Techies are using ketamine to fight their depression. June 6th, 2007.

# CHAPTER TEN:

## KETAMINE: THE FUTURE AND BEYOND

*"I never think of the future, it comes soon enough."*
—Albert Einstein

## KETAMINE CLINICS

Ketamine clearly has the potential to revolutionize the way doctors treat severe depression. It could be a game changer. If you or a loved one have struggled with depression and have had little success with traditional treatments, ketamine may be a viable option as a potential treatment. The first step is to speak to your doctor, primary-care provider, or mental-health provider. At most clinics, you will be given ketamine through an intravenous line; however, as detailed in previous chapters, you may also be given it through intramuscular injection, via a nasal spray, and by oral or sublingual tablets. From this point on we will focus our attention on intravenous ketamine infusions.

While your primary care provider will not likely be able to provide ketamine infusion therapy at their office, they can help refer you to a reputable ketamine clinic that specializes in using ketamine in humans. At a ketamine infusion center, you will undergo an initial assessment with a doctor to determine if ketamine therapy is right for you. During this assessment, the doctor will go over both your medical and mental-health histories. It is advisable to let the doctor know of any medications that you are taking. There are a few medications that can react with ketamine such as Lamictal and some benzodiazepines. It is also important to let your doctor know if you are using anything like marijuana, cocaine, or alcohol, because ketamine infusions may not go well if you are on any of these drugs. It is best to be upfront honest and transparent about any addiction or substance-abuse struggles you may be having. Addiction will not disqualify you from receiving a ketamine treatment. In fact, the treatment may provide added benefits when it comes to dealing with your addiction issues. You should also let your doctor know of any additional conditions you are dealing with such as chronic pain syndromes, PTSD, OCD, or fibromyalgia.

Once you have received the green light to move forward with ketamine, you can schedule your first treatment. Most infusions are scheduled for 30 to 45 minutes and require an intravenous line to be started. Someone will need to be with you to drive you home. Short-term side effects include a dissociative state, mild sedation, dizziness, nausea, and vomiting. These side effects are often short lived and are more likely to occur if you are on multiple substances such as marijuana or alcohol at the time of taking ketamine. The good news is there are no reported long-term side effects reported in humans with pharmaceutical grade low-dose ketamine infusions. Ketamine is often dosed based on the weight in kilograms and there is no standard or "magic dose" during an infusion. It varies from person to person. Most doctors start with a low dose and continue to adjust until they reach a dosage that effectively treats your symptoms.

During the ketamine infusion, you will need to be awake in order to receive the benefits. When used in doses that cause you to sleep, patients do not wake up with the same antidepressant effect. The number of treatments your doctor will recommend, will depend on the nature of your psychological or physical issues and how your body responds to the ketamine treatments. Many clinics will prescribe the patient three to six treatments to maximize the effects of the ketamine, but the number of treatments can vary widely from person to person. Some people require periodic treatments, while others no longer need ketamine after a single dose.

Ketamine-infusion therapy is a potentially incredible tool if you are struggling with severe depression; but using ketamine should only be done under the supervision of a medical professional. Using ketamine without the guidance of a medical doctor is strongly discouraged, dangerous, and may even be illegal depending on how you obtain it. Street ketamine is often laced with other chemicals and attempting to administer ketamine on your own can be extremely dangerous. The dissociative state caused by ketamine can, under the wrong circumstances, place you in danger. You will not know what's actually in the drug or even the dosage you are taking.

Some clinics prescribe oral ketamine to be taken at home, but this is all conducted under the supervision of a medical doctor. Ketamine is an extremely safe medication when supervised by a professional. There are hundreds of clinics nationwide in the U.S. that administer ketamine. Outpatient ketamine clinics also treat chronic pain syndromes such as fibromyalgia, migraines, complex regional pain syndrome, neuropathic pain, and radiculopathy. Many emergency departments are rediscovering the value in using ketamine for patients presenting with suicidal ideation. They also use it for sedation in other procedures like suturing wounds and setting broken bones.

## THINGS TO KNOW BEFORE GOING TO A KETAMINE CLINIC

If you have done your research, you know insurance does not typically cover ketamine treatments. Most of the costs are out of pocket. Clinics usually charge between 350 to 1,000 U.S. dollars per infusion. The prices are often higher in metropolitan areas like New York and Los Angeles and less in rural areas. The most important thing to consider in any clinic is patient safety. Most clinics are staffed by a doctor; however, in some states, a nurse practitioner or physician assistant (PA) can work independently, and there may be no physician involvement. Several nurse practitioners have attempted to open ketamine clinics, but many of them have had no in-patient hospital experience, much less any critical care or anesthesia experience. These types of clinics are poorly prepared to handle any emergency that may arise. Be sure to ask if there is a doctor present when inquiring about the clinic. If you do not feel safe or comfortable in the clinic, go somewhere else. The clinic you choose should be able to handle an emergency such as an airway or cardiac issue. Unexpected medical issues can arise, and you will want a doctor ready to handle these situations.

Ketamine treatments should be offered in conjunction with a mental-health provider. Most clinics will require a referral from a psychologist or psychiatrist. Always bring your medical records with you. If you are a parent and want your child to be treated with ketamine, most clinics will require both a primary care and psychiatry evaluation and referral. Ask if the clinic provides one-on-one monitoring. If it is one nurse or nurse practitioner administering treatments in multiple rooms, you may consider going somewhere else.

Dr. David Feifel is a board-certified neuropsychiatrist and founder the Kadima Neuropsychiatry Institute in San Diego, California. He is a professor of psychiatry at the University of California at San Diego, practices clinical psychiatry, and performs research in an academic setting. Ten years ago, he developed one of the first ketamine-infusion centers for psychiatric disorders. A prolific author, Dr. Feifel has been at the forefront of using ketamine for mental disorders. Some of his patients are funded by the *Ketamine Fund organization*. He estimates about 7 out of 10 patients improve their depression using ketamine.

Dr. Joel Friedman has been using ketamine for his patients for many years in his clinic in Hawaii. He provides each of his patients with this letter to help them understand the principles of the treatment:

### Dr. Friedman's "K" Treatments

*Currently, we are experiencing a resurgence of interest in using sub-anesthetic doses of ketamine. We have Yale Medical School largely to thank for this, as they began looking into it as a treatment for suicidal ideation, and now it's used as a treatment for PTSD and depression. Most of us in the medical world know that we have virtually no effective treatment for suicidal patients, yet Yale was finding an immediate effect. This caught my attention, and it was not long after (actually, the very next day after reading the article) a young man presented to my office with suicidal ideation as his chief complaint. He was not expecting a smile from his doctor and asked why I was grinning. I replied, "Funny that you should come today. Yesterday, I would have nothing to offer you. Today, I have a very interesting and hopeful treatment." I explained the details about ketamine and asked if he was interested. "Of course, I am." I asked him to rate his level of suicidal ideation on a scale of 1-10, with a 10 being "pass me the gun." He responded, "nine." Right there, he laid on the examining table, which is more ample than the typical examining table and quite comfortable to stretch out. I gave him headphones to block out ambient noise and an eye pillow to block out light. I then gave him 35 mg of ketamine in his vein as a quick shot. I sat and watched for the next 20 minutes, not knowing what to expect. He was completely still, and his breath* became slow and full. Outwardly, not much happened. He slowly came around after 20 minutes and took off the headphones and eyeshades. The first word out of his mouth was "Wow", which is pretty much everyone's first time reaction. We spoke a bit afterward, but finding words was difficult. It became clear this experience defies description, and this seems fairly universal; I will get to this soon. I asked him to rate his level of suicidal ideation after the ketamine, hoping I miraculously reduced it to a "six." He looked puzzled and responded, "zero". I asked again, thinking he did not understand my question. He repeated, zero. Now, it was my turn to be speechless. Going from a nine to a zero in 20 minutes, in terms of wanting to kill oneself, was, simply put, a miracle. I had never seen or heard of this before, nor had any of my colleagues. I knew we were onto something very special and I have been doing ketamine sessions ever since for conditions which include depression, PTSD, bipolar illness and anxiety. The only mental conditions in which I will not use ketamine are schizophrenia and Borderline Personality Disorder. This is not a treatment for anyone who does not have a decent grip on reality. I screen every patient and will not use ketamine if I am uncomfortable. The results have been close to universally beneficial. The level of benefit ranges from mild to life changing. Sometimes, there is just one session, and, for others, it can be a weekly affair. The mechanics of a session are straightforward. There are three ways I administer ketamine: quick intravenous (IV) push, slow intravenous drip, and intramuscular injection. For first time patients, I use a 35 mg IV push. The slow IV drip is administered over 30 minutes and the dose varies from 50 to 80 mg. The intramuscular dose is given in the deltoid muscle in a dose of 50-60 mg. These have proven to be very safe dosages requiring no monitoring devices, and no patient has ever experienced any difficulties in terms of dosage. It is very important to discuss the ketamine experience in terms the patient can understand. I first explain this will be unlike any experience they have ever had, and it is very strong and unique. Going into it with comfort is essential. Being a first-time experience, it is natural to be anxious. "What will happen? Will I succeed or fail? Can I handle it?" This is an experience that cannot be controlled, and control freaks can have a real hard time letting go to the extent needed for the session. If, in speaking to such a one, they convey an inability or unwillingness to surrender control for the duration of the session (about 30 minutes), then I simply back away from using ketamine until they feel they can let the experience unfold.

*I realized I needed to experience a 'K' session myself, so I knew firsthand what it does and what one experiences. I quickly saw what this medicine does experientially. The details of its effects on neurotransmitters and on the brain interest me little, but I am happy others are looking into this aspect. I have always been interested in its practical applications, as this is the essence and focus of my clinical practice. In describing the experience of ketamine, we are all at a loss for words for reasons to which I will get. Often, the best we can do is to rely on metaphor; descriptions will vary depending on the person, their level of spiritual understanding, and their poetic inclination and ability. Within a minute of injecting the ketamine, a very odd sensation occurs. Many describe this as an OBE or out-of-body experience, and it is. It happens with such abruptness the patient needs to be prepared for this as best as possible. It is very important, at this moment, to recognize what is happening and to let go as much and as deeply as possible. It can feel like dying, and it is important prior to taking 'K' the patient understands they are NOT dying even though it may feel that way. All bodily functions continue to operate normally, and conscious awareness is not needed for the body to function during the session. While some experience their OBE as dying, others experience it as a great liberation, as if they have come home. These are the ones who don't want to come back. After the abrupt OBE, there follows an experience which varies between people and within the individual during multiple sessions. No two sessions are alike. Some are dark and others are very light. Within a session, some start out dark and then it all becomes very light. I have never seen it the other way around. Sometimes, there is a story, other times, a sequence of scenes, or geometric shapes, or bright colors. Sometimes, the feeling is blissful and expansive. Other times, it can be as if nothing happened. On questioning the latter type of non-experience, there will always be some nugget to be extracted with a little digging and reflection.*

*Dark experiences are often followed by blissful ones, and the point must be made there is as much to gain from one as the other. I will allow some talk after a session, but only if the patient needs such. Once one does a session, this is an experience beyond the realm of words. It is unnecessary to talk afterward, and it sometimes serves to bring one out of their post 'K' state of mind. One thing I have noticed is a complete absence of fear during the session, despite some anxiety going into it. It takes a week (sometimes even more), to integrate the experience. I always allow the patient* to determine if more sessions are needed. It seems everyone knows if repeat sessions are needed, and they also know when their time with 'K' is done. I feel careful attention to set, and setting is critical to a successful outcome. Careful explanation of what to expect must be accompanied by a safe, quiet, and serene setting. I prefer a more natural setting and find patients are very comfortable in such a setting. I dislike a clinical setting for a 'K' session and all the monitoring devices and high-tech approaches I find unnecessary and only adding to the expense. What exactly is happening during a 'K' session? Two key events take place. From a brain perspective, one experiences a 're-set'. This is a word coming from patients. This reset can allow a shift in the basic mood or affect; the default setting in the brain. If chronically depressed, one can see a change to less time being depressed or no depression at all. If it is PTSD the patient has, they can see the vanishing of that trauma, as if an eraser did its job on the part of the brain where the particular trauma memory was stored. This can happen in a single session, and some choose to do multiple sessions, each time getting the reset they so fervently desire and need.

The response is variable among individuals regarding duration of benefit. One gets an antidepressant effect and a reset with each session, and the effect seems to be cumulative. Patients will often describe their results in terms of a reset, and this is most dramatic with suicidal patients. I know of no other modality that even approaches the profundity of ketamine's ability to reset the brain. While the brain reset is so beneficial and therapeutic, there is a parallel phenomenon that is more intriguing and profound. This is the OBE one experiences and contextualizing this is important. One feels a complete loss of a sense of self. There is a temporary (15-30 minutes) loss of the mind/body, which we call the ego. A permanent loss of ego we know as death and under the influence of ketamine, we get a sneak preview of what it will be like when we die. Most patients leave with a much more relaxed and less fearful attitude surrounding their death, perceiving there is a realm to which we return that seems to be eternal. This alone is worth the price of admission. We are all entrapped within our ego and to be completely free of it for even a brief period is invariably liberating and instructive. Many have very amazing and fantastic journeys which can help inform their daily existence. If our ego disappears, what is it that is left? I recognize this as the realm of the soul, which we are *oblivious to in our day-to-day existence. During the 'K' experience, we get to visit the realm of pure soul unencumbered by ego. I know of no other means short of a near death experience that allows us this very special privilege. This visit to the realm of soul will have many speak of coming home. Our true home to which we will permanently return upon death of the body. This aspect of the journey also speaks to our true identity... Who am I? Most leave with a profound peace and sense of calm which often permeates their ego existence. In this age of anxiety, what could be better or more profound. When embarking on a ketamine journey, always send the prayer, 'Connect with Source'. You will.*

*Source:* © Joel Friedman M.D.

## KETAMINE FOUNDATIONS

Foundations such as the Ketamine Fund (www.ketaminefund.org) deserve a special mention. Entrepreneurs and filmmakers Zappy Zapolin and Warren Gumpel founded the Ketamine Fund as a non-profit organization that funds ketamine treatments for veterans in need. Zapolin and Gumpel have an intense interest in helping veterans with mental illness. The goal of the Ketamine Fund is to bring down U.S. veteran suicide rates by 70 percent. The Ketamine Fund has aligned with dozens of clinics around the country that are providing needed ketamine treatments to veterans. Their mission is to reach service members returning from duty experiencing severe mental trauma such as suicidal thoughts and ideation. Gumpel highlights the need to reduce the nearly 20 suicides per day by military service members and save millions of Americans from suffering the devastation so many have experienced. The Ketamine Fund organization prearranges the cost of the ketamine infusions. Veterans benefit greatly from ketamine because they have experienced so much trauma, and they deserve this help. Zapolin gives the example of one veteran who was on 22 different medications from the VA hospital, and, after a series of ketamine treatments, he was able to stop all of his medications, go home, and have a relationship with his kids for the first time in 10 years. These transitions happen so fast, and you don't have to wait around for weeks or months to see the effects. How else could you do this besides going to a country like Peru, sitting with a shaman, and experiencing deep integration with ayahuasca?

Zapolin and Gumpel are also the filmmakers behind the psychedelic advocacy film *The Reality of Truth* with actress Michelle Rodriguez and Dr. Deepak Chopra. Over six million people have viewed the documentary since its release. The movie has certainly influenced a significant number of people. Some have said things like, "I was going to commit suicide, then I saw this movie and I started doing plant medicine, and it totally changed my life" and "I was a drug addict and homeless and I found plant medicine through this movie." Zappy and Warren also recently produced *Lamar Odom - Reborn*, a movie about Lamar Odom's path to recovery. Lamar Odom played for the Los Angeles Lakers, winning championships in 2009 and 2010. He was also married to Khloe Kardashian for seven years. Battling mental-health and addiction, Lamar's life spiraled out of control in 2015, when he was found unconscious in a Nye county brothel in Nevada. On life support, Odom lived through multiple strokes and heart attacks while in the hospital and has been called a "walking miracle" by doctors. He survived the ordeal and took action to seek treatment for patterns of addiction after years of trauma and the overdose that nearly took his life. The film highlights Lamar's journey using ketamine, plant medicine, and daily practice to overcome addiction, anxiety, and trauma.

In an interview with Zappy and Warren, he said his focus is on ketamine and how to make it more accessible to everyone. The current landscape shows ketamine is more accessible than other psychoactive agents such as psilocybin and MDMA. "Psilocybin and MDMA both have great potential, but they are not available throughout the country, whereas ketamine is available now. It's FDA approved, and there are hundreds of clinics using ketamine for depression and suicide," Zappy says. Warren Gumpel says ketamine saved his life as well. Before ketamine he had considered suicide, and it was not until he found ketamine through Dr. Brooks in New York that he overcame his suicidal ideation.

## KETAMD

The goal of KetaMD is to make ketamine treatments mainstream and bring them safely into the homes of patients, increasing accessibility. Spravato and ketamine infusions must be done in a doctor's office, which greatly limits the accessibility to patients. Ketamine safely breaks the patterns of SAAD (suicide, anxiety, addiction, and depression), PTSD, and other mental-health issues. As the U.S. is currently going through one of the worst mental-health epidemics in human history, KetaMD is a doctor-directed organization that sees patients through a health visit, virtual or physical, and then arranges for ketamine to be delivered to the patient's home to be taken orally under the supervision of a qualified health practitioner. The KetaMD team comprises doctors, nurses, and staff who are deeply dedicated to sharing ketamine with the world. The core values of KetaMD are the mission of healing and an unyielding belief in the life-transforming power of ketamine treatment.

### Case: CEO of an IT Company - Anonymous

Mr. A is a successful CEO of an international cybersecurity company. He is also a Vietnam veteran with significant PTSD. He explains he has been using ketamine with his personal physician for many years. The ketamine treatments helped him with his PTSD, gain introspection, and opened his mind, translating into better performance as a CEO and in his personal life. Mr. A recorded a detailed analysis of his ketamine experiences. He writes:

*The feeling of the loss of control is the beginning of the separation of mind, probably the neurons firing; a kind of "taking off." Last night, I discovered I still had the cognitive control to direct my mind in whatever I chased. I let go of my surroundings and thoughts that were influencing the direction and my cognitive thinking and chose to direct it deliberately to myself and on my issues. I chose to focus the activity on my current stress and issues with all the things troubling me. I could dissect my issues and rearrange them in another way. My happiness and health became the central core or the true intent that emerged as the director of the experience.*

*I realized, after a bit, all these things troubling my life, so extreme, were of my doing. To the point, I understood all I had to do was stop the way I have been choosing to embrace these problems; and simply choosing instead to let go of the unhealthy ways I dealt with it. By doing so would simply allow me to deal with these issues and be happy. At the same time I was not delusional. I felt a new reality of these issues and how I have dealt with them in my reality, but without the stress. There are a bunch of things I need to handle, and I am capable of doing so. That creates my anxiety, fear, depression, and unhealthy responses. All I have to do is let go of these things within myself and keep happiness and health as the center point. I can still perform and achieve and be healthy. Furthermore, the result will be superior. This was a breakthrough in how I am supposed to manage the treatment experience and get the actual value out of it. This time was not a trippy experience that helps in other ways which it has in the past. If the person doing the treatment understands what I learned last night, it can be of extraordinary benefit, well beyond what I have experienced before. I think I finally got it. What is unique about this treatment is it is not an uncontrolled trip. My mind still has control, and I can direct it. If a person doing this does not realize or have any cognitive strength to do the treatment, it may not be good for them; because that person will not be going into the treatment with a direct purpose and intent, weakness of mind, and it will take you somewhere else.*

*For me, doing the treatment should start with a conducive and unobtrusive environment with a purpose on which you want to focus. Unlike other drugs you cannot control, this one you can. Even when the brain is firing off with force in a way you have never experienced, you still have fundamental control if you choose. You need to be aware of this; it is a bit tricky, but you have control. It is not acid!*

### Case Example: Psychologist - Ashley

*Ashley Clayton had undergone 17 ECT treatments for her chronic major depression. Even the simplest cognitive tasks were challenging. Three ECT sessions were of the more aggressive bi-frontal type. Ashley's depression never lifted. Realizing the last possible treatments available for her disease were failing, it was only a matter of time before her illness would inevitably kill her. Ashley's childhood was scarred with serious trauma, resulting in depression, PTSD, and suicide attempts. Despite her depression, she made it through high school and into college. After graduating from college, she enrolled in a master's program for psychology. Things seemed to be finally going well for Ashley. She even got married. In 2014, stressful life events rekindled the past trauma and set off a depressive episode. As a result, her mental-health declined. Experiencing anhedonia, the inability to feel pleasure, she started therapy and was put on medications. "Nothing worked," she recalls. She took leave from her work, and this was devastating. Desperate, she researched ketamine and connected with Dr. Gerard Sanacora at Yale University, who enrolled her in a ketamine trial. She went home to sleep off the treatment, and awoke the following morning, "feeling dramatically different... a miracle." She felt like going for a run, something that she had rarely done before. She said she even regained her love for her husband, which she had lost because of her depression. However, approximately two weeks later, Ashly woke up to a full-blown episode of depression. She contemplated suicide again. Unable to receive ketamine again because of financial constraints and Yale University policies, she was again offered ECT treatments. Admitting herself to a psychiatric hospital, she began a series of 17 ECT treatments, which ultimately did not help her depression, and the induced seizures were affecting her thinking. Finally, a few days before Christmas, she received her next dose of ketamine - nearly a year since she had received the first. After four weekly treatments, Ashley felt like she had after the first ketamine treatment. Her psychiatrists were convinced the only way to treat Ashley's depression was through ketamine infusions. Her doctors convinced the hospital administrators to provide her with free care over the long term. Since this time, Ashley has received ketamine treatments every two to three weeks, depending on her symptoms. Ashley states, "Ketamine not only saved my life, but has restored me to the joys and pains of full living. I feel, for the first time in my life, like there is air to breathe." She has been treated with ketamine for many years now. For the time being, she is happy she and her doctors know ketamine can keep her depression and thoughts of ending her life at bay.*

Source: Brain & Behavior mag 2019

## Case: The Dennis Hartman story - Dr. Brooks

This is an incredible story about a man suffering from major refractory depressive disorder his entire life, associated with traumatic stress disorder which resulted from childhood abuse. Dennis describes his existence as "misery" and says, "Living with my depression feels like pain." He further explains that it's not something you can show to someone, like pointing to an injury or a wound, but it feels very much like physical pain. Dennis recalls, *"I knew I had a problem by the time I was in 7th grade. I had a very traumatic childhood and spent it in a state of intense fear. By the time I reached adolescence, I had a pretty good idea I wasn't able to do things like other kids could."* Dennis Hartman spent decades working through a roster of medical and therapeutic treatments for depression. He tried every known depressive therapy (SSRIs, SNRIs, tricyclics, benzodiazepines, etc.) notes Dennis, "A lot of my energy in life has been spent trying to get relief from this pain. On my worst days, I lost the energy. I didn't have the ability or the strength to inhabit that character anymore... I just didn't see any way around it." In his mid-40s, Hartman decided he was going to end his life, believing whole-heartedly it was a humane and reasonable thing to do. He explains, "There's only so much untreatable suffering that one person can be expected to endure in their lifetime." He chose a date several months away to get his affairs in order and avoid causing his nephew trauma during school finals. Awaiting his date, he heard of an experimental trial using ketamine to treat depression and PTSD. He applied and was immediately accepted. *"The day I received my infusion, my symptoms were raging; anxiety, anhedonia (the inability to experience pleasure), and insomnia. They turned on the drip, and I was in a dreamlike state; like a spectator watching my thoughts unfold in front of me. Within 15 to 20 minutes of the end of the infusion, I knew something was different. They asked me questions to monitor my mood, and I had trouble pinpointing my symptoms."* Within a couple of hours of the infusion, Dennis had a clear awareness something was missing. He explains, "It didn't strike me as a wave of massive relief. It didn't feel like something was added to me, like I had superpowers. I didn't have euphoria. It was a gradual realization over a few hours something was missing and what was missing was something horrible. If you suffer from lifelong depression as I have, and it's all you've ever known, it becomes part of your identity. You just feel the world is all about pain, and when I got relief from my first infusion, it was like being emancipated." Since discovering this treatment, Dennis has become a tireless advocate of ketamine therapy, establishing, and running the Ketamine Advocacy Network, to spread awareness of the treatment and connect potential patients with doctors who provide it. As of 2018, there are now over 250 clinics and 1,000 practitioners in the U.S. offering ketamine therapy.

Source: Wolfson M.D., Phil. The Ketamine Papers: Science, Therapy, and Transformation (pp. 293-294). Multidisciplinary Association for Psychedelic Studies.

## KETAMINE FUTURE AND BEYOND

Ketamine is the first antidepressant medication to be cleared by the FDA in many years. The excitement in the psychiatric community is evident with the discovery of a new class of antidepressants, the glutamate-antagonist arylcyclohexylamines, of which ketamine is the prototype. One overbearing issue surrounding ketamine is cost and accessibility. The cost of ketamine infusions is just out of reach for most of the population. Many travel long distances to receive ketamine. Insurance companies do not generally reimburse ketamine treatments, except for Spravato, which must be pre-approved and administered in an office setting. Although ketamine itself will probably not become the next generation of antidepressants, it seems numerous other members of the arylcyclohexylamines class will be presented as the next generation of anti-anxiety drugs, mood stabilizers, and procognitive agents. The recent interest in ketamine may eventually bring psychedelic psychotherapy somewhat closer to the mainstream of psychiatry and neurology.

## OTHER PSYCHEDELICS

A word about other psychedelics like MDMA, LSD, and psilocybin. There is a lot of attention about these psychedelic drugs in several books, such as Michael Pollan's, *How to Change Your Mind*, and *The Door of Perception* by Aldous Huxley. These books highlight how drugs like LSD and psilocybin can give you a psychedelic experience and change your life. Ketamine provides this experience as well at sub-anesthetic doses, with a pharmaceutical grade product in a controlled setting. A study was done where the researchers aimed to categorize their psychedelic experience into 11 kinds of phenomena. Participants were given ketamine, LSD, MDMA, and psilocybin in different orders. They discovered that the ratings for LSD, ketamine, and psilocybin were quite similar. There were some differences between the drugs. Ketamine scored the highest on the out-of-body experience. MDMA was found to be more euphoric than profound in a classic sense of psychedelic or mind enhancing. The rapid antidepressant effects of psilocybin and ketamine are similar. A recent paper from Johns Hopkins School of Medicine about the effects of psilocybin assisted therapy on major depressive disorder (MDD) showed efficacy in treating MDD with psilocybin.

Author and podcaster, Tim Ferris is a big advocate of using psychedelic therapy with ketamine and psilocybin. Dave Asprey, Founder of Bulletproof Coffee, a company specializing in human optimization and bio-hacking, is no stranger to ketamine. Asprey has used ketamine and understands the positive effects on his brain. In a podcast about ketamine, Dave describes how one of his colleagues overcame her lifelong fear of needles with a single ketamine treatment. If she was presented with a needle, she fainted on the spot. While on ketamine, she could see the needle pushing on the IV catheter and afterward, she said her fear was gone.

Current research is focusing on the development of ketamine derivatives. Examples in this area include the novel antidepressants under the names Rapastinel and Rislenemdaz. They bind to the NMDA receptor, similar to ketamine, with less psychoactive effects. Both drugs showed promise in phase 2 studies but were ultimately pulled from development after later phase trials failed to show a benefit. Medications like Rapastinel and Rislenemdaz show the pharmaceutical companies are currently developing drugs that use the same mechanisms as ketamine.

The Nevada-based foundation, BetterU.foundation, is a leading voice of mental-health; their goals are to end mental-health stigmas and improve mental-health access. On their website, they show multiple pictures of celebrities who have mental illness and/or have committed suicide. Robin Williams is prominently featured. They are working towards reducing the stigma associated with mental illness through broad forms of treatment including psychiatry, psychotherapy, and psychedelic therapy. One of the founders, Derek Du Chesne, says, "Raising awareness will decrease the discrimination against people with mental illness. This is why a lot of people never seek help and end up taking their life." The foundation is working to provide free introductory mental-health care, emphasize lifestyle changes, and provide psychiatric and psychedelic services. The foundation is being started by professional baseball player Drew Robinson (see Chapter 1), stuntman, actor and entrepreneur Derek Du Chesne, and Las Vegas psychiatrist Sam Zand.

We have seen many clinics, foundations, emergency departments, mental-health hotlines, books, self-enlightenment clinics, and more embrace the use of ketamine. Ketamine is certainly here to stay, but how we will move forward remains a question. Certainly, ketamine will move into the emergency departments and pediatric mental-health spaces. Pharmaceutical companies are developing derivatives of ketamine that avoid the psychoactive effects and keep the mental-health effects. We are also seeing ketamine moving out of the clinics and transitioning to home treatment through organizations like KetaMD and Better U. Many physicians are open to using ketamine for suicidal ideation; however, there are still some concerns. The major concern is ketamine is a substantial drug of abuse worldwide. Despite the robust evidence ketamine offers short-term benefits to the individual suffering from possibly fatal mood disorders because of high suicide risk, this treatment has not yet undergone the multiple, large-scale trials needed to determine the durability and safety of long-term treatment. Suicide is always going to be a major health issue. The COVID-19 crisis has only fueled the mental-health crisis, contributing to it. Given the exacerbation of mental-health disparity, the continuing development of depression, and the increase in both suicide ideation and execution, it is important to know that there are options available to relieve those symptoms. Ketamine has emerged as the one drug and very viable option that can alleviate suicidal ideation, and possibly save your loved one's life.

# BIBLIOGRAPHY

**Chapter 1**

1. Chalabi, Mona. "How Bad Is US Gun Violence? These Charts Show the Scale of the Problem." The Guardian. Guardian News and Media, October 5, 2017. https://www.theguardian.com/us-news/2017/oct/05/us-gun-violence-charts-data.

2. Drew Robinson in discussion with the author, April 2020.

3. https://www.who.int/teams/mental-health-and-substance-use/suicide-data.

4. https://www.who.int/teams/mental-health-and-substance-use/suicide-data

5. https://suicidology.org/facts-and-statistics/

6. Passan, Jeff. "San Francisco Giants Outfielder Drew Robinson's Remarkable Second Act." ESPN. ESPN Internet Ventures, May 12, 2021. https://www.espn.com/mlb/story/_/id/30800732/san-francisco-giants-outfielder-drew-robinson-remarkable-second-act.

7. "Suicide Data." World Health Organization. World Health Organization. Accessed June 06, 2021.

8. Sidhu, S. UNICEF: An additional 6.7 million children under 5 could suffer from wasting this year due to COVID-19. UNICEF New York. 27 July 2020.

**Chapter 2**

1. "2019 National Veteran Suicide Prevention Annual Report." PDF file. 2019. https://www.mentalhealth.va.gov/docs/data-sheets/2019/2019_National_Veteran_Suicide_Prevention_Annual_Report_508.pdf

2. Bendavid E, Oh C, Bhattacharya J, Ioannidis JPA. Assessing mandatory stay-at-home and business closure effects on the spread of COVID-19. Eur J Clin Invest. 2021 Apr;51(4):e13484. doi: 10.1111/eci.13484. Epub 2021 Feb 1. PMID: 33400268; PMCID: PMC7883103.

3. Czeisler, Mark. Mental Health, Substance Abuse, and Suicidal Ideation During the COVID-19 Pandemic - United States, June 24-30, 2020. Morbidity and Mortality Weekly Report, CDC, Vol. 69., No. 32.

4. De Becker, Gavin. 2000. The Gift of Fear. London, England: Bloomsbury Publishing PLC.

5. EUROMOMO / https://www.euromomo.eu/ Accessed April 2021

6.  Gianfranco Alicandro, et al. "Excess Deaths Associated with Covid-19 Pandemic in 2020: Age and Sex Disaggregated Time Series Analysis in 29 High Income Countries." The BMJ. British Medical Journal Publishing Group, May 19, 2021. https://www.bmj.com/content/373/bmj.n1137.

7.  Green, Erica. Surge of Student Suicides Pushes Las Vegas Schools to Reopen. New York Times. January 24th, 2021. https://www.nytimes.com/2021/01/24/us/politics/student-suicides-nevada-coronavirus.html

8.  Hayden Hunstable Website / https://www.youtube.com/watch?v=VJTHFhVyyqI

9.  Kelly, Jack. The Pandemic Has Caused An Increase in Anxiety, Stress, Depression And Suicides. Forbes Magazine. Aug. 18th, 2020. https://www.forbes.com/sites/jackkelly/2020/08/18/the-pandemic-has-caused-an-increase-in-anxiety-stress-depression-and-suicides/?sh=313b327c5863

10. Kessler RC, Bauer MS, Bishop TM, et al. Using Administrative Data to Predict Suicide After Psychiatric Hospitalization in the Veterans Health Administration System. Front Psychiatry. 2020;11:390. Published 2020 May 6.

11. https://ketamineinstitute.com/depression/olives-view-of-heaven/, accessed July 15th, 2020.

12. Nevada Governor Steve Sisolak State of Nevada Address November 11th, 2020 / https://www.8newsnow.com/news/local-news/4th-ccsd-suicide-raises-concern-of-mental-health-crisis-during-covid-19-pandemic/?fbclid=IwAR1iAwnsBX kBfCymL0ap4K3DDw6zdI79f55-7Mb8pEgQ4vQg_QX9hYKVdLE

13. Nørgaard, Sarah K et al. "Real-time monitoring shows substantial excess all-cause mortality during second wave of COVID-19 in Europe, October to December 2020."

14. Sakamoto H, Ishikane M, Ghaznavi C, Ueda P. Assessment of Suicide in Japan During the COVID-19 Pandemic vs Previous Years. JAMA Netw Open. 2021;4(2):e2037378. doi:10.1001/jamanetworkopen.2020.37378

15. "2019 National Veteran Suicide Prevention Annual Report." PDF file. 2019. https://www.mentalhealth.va.gov/docs/data-sheets/2019/2019_National_Veteran_Suicide_Prevention_Annual_Report_508.pdf

16. "Vital Signs: Trends in State Suicide Rates - United States, 1999–2016 and Circumstances Contributing to Suicide - 27 States, 2015." Centers for Disease Control and Prevention Weekly Report. Centers for Disease Control and Prevention, June 10, 2019.

## Chapter 3

1.  "2020 Global Food Report On Food Crisis." World Food Programme. 2020. https://docs.wfp.org/api/documents/WFP-0000114546/download/?_ga=2.119886030.77193592.1623738808-936356042.1623738808

2.  Ahmad, Farida B, and Robert N Anderson. "The Leading Causes of Death in the US for 2020." JAMA. JAMA Network, May 11, 2021. https://jamanetwork.com/journals/jama/fullarticle/2778234.

3.  "Archived: WHO Timeline - COVID-19." World Health Organization.

World Health Organization. Accessed June 06, 2021. https://www. who.int/news/item/27-04-2020-who-timeline---covid-19.

4. Assi, Rima, Mael de Calan, Akash Kaul, and Aurelien Vincent. "Closing the $30 Trillion Gap: Acting Now to Manage Fiscal Deficits during and beyond the COVID-19 Crisis." McKinsey & Company. McKinsey & Company, May 13, 2021. https://www. mckinsey.com/industries/public-and-social-sector/our-insights/closing-the-30-trillion-gap-acting-now-to-manage-fiscal-deficits-during-and-beyond-the-covid-19-crisis.

5. Atlas, Scott W. "A Pandemic of Misinformation." The Wall Street Journal. Dow Jones & Company, December 21, 2020. https://www. wsj.com/articles/a-pandemic-of-misinformation-11608570640.

6. Barr, Luke. "Record Number of US Police Officers Died by Suicide in 2019, Advocacy Group Says." ABC News. ABC News Network, January 2, 2020. Accessed June 06, 2021. https://abcnews.go.com/Politics/record-number-us-police-officers-died-suicide-2019/story?id=68031484.

7. Balaji M, Vijayakumar L, Phillips M, Panse S, Santre M, Pathare S, Patel V. The Young Lives Matter study protocol: A case-control study of the determinants of suicide attempts in young people in India. Wellcome Open Res. 2020 Nov 3;5:262.

8. Benen, Steve. "For 19th Straight Week, Unemployment Filings Top 1 Million." MSNBC. NBC Universal News Group, July 30, 2020. https://www.msnbc.com/rachel-maddow-show/19th-straight-week-unemployment-filings-top-1-million-n1235299.

9. Berreson, Alex. Unreported Truths About COVID-19 and Lockdowns. June 4th, 2020.

10. "Coronavirus Cases." Worldometer. Accessed June 06, 2021. https://www.worldometers.info/coronavirus/.

11. "Coronavirus Patients Describe Symptoms: 'The Fever Is so High That You Hallucinate.'" CBS News. CBS Interactive, March 17, 2020. https://www.cbsnews.com/news/coronavirus-symptoms-fever-dry-cough-shortness-of-breath/.

12. Cronin, Christopher and Evans, William N., Nursing Home Quality, Covid-19 Deaths, and Excess Mortality (October 2020). NBER Working Paper No. w28012, Available at SSRN: https://ssrn.com/abstract=3723250

13. Dastagir, Alia E. "More and More Americans Are Dying by Suicide. What Are We Missing?" USA Today. Gannett Satellite Information Network, January 30, 2020. https://www.usatoday.com/story/news/nation/2020/01/30/u-s-suicide-rate-rose-again-2018-how-can-suicide-prevention-save-lives/4616479002/.

14. Davis MA, Cher BAY, Friese CR, Bynum JPW. Association of US Nurse and Physician Occupation With Risk of Suicide. JAMA Psychiatry. 2021 Apr 14;78(6):1–8.

15. De Becker, Gavin. 2000. The Gift of Fear. London, England: Bloomsbury Publishing PLC.

16. Garai, Shuvabrata. "Student Suicides Rising, 28 Lives Lost Every Day." The Hindu. The Hindu, January 29, 2020. Accessed June 06, 2021. https://www.thehindu.com/news/national/student-suicides-rising-28-lives-lost-every-day/article30685085.ece.

17. Ioannidis, JPA. "Reconciling estimates of global spread and infection fatality rates

of COVID-19: An overview of systematic evaluations." Eur J Clin Invest, 2021.

18. Ioannidis, J. Infection fatality rate of COVID-19 inferred from seroprevalence data. Bulletin of the World Health Organization. Oct 14th, 2020.

19. Iob, Eleonora, Andrew Steptoe, and Daisy Fancourt. "Abuse, Self-Harm and Suicidal Ideation in the UK during the COVID-19 Pandemic." The British journal of psychiatry: the journal of mental science. Cambridge University Press, October 2020. https://www.ncbi.nlm.nih.gov/pmc/articles/PMC7360935/.

20. Janiri D, Doucet GE, Pompili M, Sani G, Luna B, Brent DA, Frangou S. Risk and protective factors for childhood suicidality: a US population-based study. Lancet Psychiatry. 2020 Apr;7(4):317-326

21. Malhotra, A. The 21-Day Immunity Plan. 2020. Yellow Kite Books.

22. Mamelund,SE. Effects of the Spanish Influenza Pandemic of 1918-19 on Later Life Mortality of Norwegian Cohorts Born About 1900. 2003.

23. Moore, Mark. China pressured WHO to delay global coronavirus warning: report. New York Post. May 10th, 2020. https://nypost.com/2020/05/10/china-pressured-who-to-delay-global-coronavirus-warning/

24. Police Executive Research Forum. Critical Issues in Policing Series. An Occupational Risk: What Every Police Agency Should Do To Prevent Suicide Among Its Officers. October 2019.

25. "Provisional Death Counts for Coronavirus Disease 2019 (COVID-19)." Centers for Disease Control and Prevention. Centers for Disease Control and Prevention, June 17, 2021. https://www.cdc.gov/nchs/nvss/vsrr/covid19/index.htm.

26. Rabin, Roni Caryn. "U.S. Suicides Declined Over All in 2020 but May Have Risen Among People of Color." The New York Times. The New York Times, April 15, 2021. https://www.nytimes.com/2021/04/15/health/coronavirus-suicide-cdc.html.

27. Reger, M. Suicide Mortality and Coronavirus Disease 2019 - A Perfect Storm? JAMA Psychiatry. November 2020. Volume 77, Number 11.

28. Riley, Charles. "60 Million Europeans Could Suffer Furloughs, Layoffs or Wage Cuts." CNN. Cable News Network, April 19, 2020. https://www.cnn.com/2020/04/19/business/europe-jobs-coronavirus-mckinsey/index.html

29. Schippers, Michaéla C. "For the Greater Good? The Devastating Ripple Effects of the Covid-19 Crisis." Frontiers. Frontiers, September 9, 2020. https://www.frontiersin.org/articles/10.3389/fpsyg.2020.577740/full.

30. Singer, J. The American Association of Suicidology. https://suicidology.org/2020/11/02/covidandsuicide/

31. Strobel, W. Hinshaw, D. Intelligence on Sick Staff at Wuhan Lab Fuels Debate on Covid-19 Origin. The Wall Street Journal. May 23rd, 2021.

32. Taubenberger JK, Morens DM. "1918 Influenza: the mother of all pandemics." Emerg Infect Dis, 2006. 12(1):15-22.

33.  The Hindu. Student suicides rising, 28 lives lost every day. The Hindu [Internet]. [cited 2020 Aug 27], https://www.thehindu.com/ news/national/student-suicides-rising-28- lives-lost-every-day/article3

34.  Wang, Selina, Rebecca Wright, and Yoko Wakatsuki. "In Japan, More People Died from Suicide Last Month than from Covid in All of 2020." CNN. Cable News Network, November 30, 2020. https://www.cnn.com/2020/11/28/asia/japan-suicide-women-covid-dst-intl-hnk/index.html.

35.  Zetzsche, Dirk A, and Roberta Consiglio. "One Million or One Hundred Million Casualties? – The Impact of the COVID-19 Crisis on the Least Developed and Developing Countries." University of Luxembourg, Law Working Paper Series 2020-008. SSRN, May 10, 2020. https://papers.ssrn.com/sol3/papers.cfm?abstract_id=3597657

**Chapter 4**

1.  Agence France Press. New York School Shutdown Angers Parents As Gyms, Bars Stay Open. Nov 19th, 2020.

2.  Ahmed, M. Z., Ahmed, O., Aibao, Z., Hanbin, S., Siyu, L., & Ahmad, A. (2020). Epidemic of COVID-19 in China and associated Psychological Problems. Asian journal of psychiatry, 51.

3.  Alamri HS, Algarni A, Shehata SF, Al Bshabshe A, Alshehri NN, ALAsiri AM, Hussain AH, Alalmay AY, Alshehri EA, Alqarni Y, Saleh NF. Prevalence of Depression, Anxiety, and Stress among the General Population in Saudi Arabia during Covid-19 Pandemic. Int J Environ Res Public Health. 2020 Dec 9;17(24):9183.

4.  Allen, TR. An outbreak of common colds at an Antarctic base after seventeen weeks of complete isolation. The Journal of Hygiene Vol. 71, No. 4 (Dec. 1973), pp. 657-667.

5.  Bachmann S. Epidemiology of suicide and the psychiatric perspective. Int. J. Environ. Res. Public Health. 2018:15

6.  Barbisch D., Koenig K.L., Shih F.Y. Is there a case for quarantine? Perspectives from SARS to ebola. Disaster Med. Public Health Prep. 2015;9:547–553.

7.  Bernstein, W. The Delusion of Crowds: Why People Go Mad in Groups. Feb 23rd, 2021. Tantor Audio.

8.  Belluck, P. A new coronavirus threat to children. New York Times. May 6th, 2020.

9.  Berreson, Alex. Unreported Truths About COVID-19 and Lockdowns. June 4th, 2020.

10.  Brooks, S et al. The Psychological Impact of Quarantine and How to Reduce it: A rapid review of the evidence. VOLUME 395, ISSUE 10227, P912-920, MARCH 14, 2020.

11.  Centers for Disease Control and Prevention; 2020. Coronavirus Disease 2019 (COVID-19).

12.  Czeisler, Mark. Mental Health, Substance Abuse, and Suicidal Ideation During the COVID-19 Pandemic - United States, June 24-30, 2020. Morbidity and Mortality Weekly Report, CDC, Vol. 69., No. 32.

13.  Deutsch, D. (2011). The beginning of infinity: explanations that transform the world. 1st American ed. New York: Viking.

14.  Drug related deaths in the Nordic countries – Revision of the statistical definition. NOMESCO Nordic Medico Statistical Committee 108:2017.

15.  EUROMOMO / https://www.euromomo.eu/ Accessed April 2021

16.  Gladwell, Malcolm. 2019. Talking to strangers: what we should know about the people we don't know.

17.  Hawryluck, L., Gold, W. L., Robinson, S., Pogorski, S., Galea, S., & Styra, R. (2004). SARS control and psychological effects of quarantine, Toronto, Canada. Emerging infectious diseases, 10(7), 1206–1212.

18.  Ioannidis, J. Infection fatality rate of COVID-19 inferred from seroprevalence data. Bulletin of the World Health Organization. Oct 14th, 2020.

19.  Jacobson NC, Lekkas D, Price G, Heinz MV, Song M, O'Malley AJ, Barr PJ. Flattening the Mental Health Curve: COVID-19 Stay-at-Home Orders Are Associated With Alterations in Mental Health Search Behavior in the United States. JMIR Ment Health. 2020 Jun 1;7(6).

20.  Jacobson, S. H., & Jokela, J. A. (2020). Non-COVID-19 excess deaths by age and gender in the United States during the first three months of the COVID-19 pandemic. Public health, 189, 101–103.

21.  Kahil, K et al. Suicide during COVID-19 and other major international respiratory outbreaks: A systematic review. Asian journal of psychiatry, vol. 56, 2021.

22.  Kailash Satyarthi Children's Foundation. A Study on Impact of Lockdown and Economic Disruption on Poor Rural Households with Special Reference to Children. 2020.

23.  Leeb RT, Bitsko RH, Radhakrishnan L, Martinez P, Njai R, Holland KM. Mental Health-Related Emergency Department Visits Among Children Aged <18 Years During the COVID-19 Pandemic - United States, January 1-October 17, 2020. MMWR Morb Mortal Wkly Rep. 2020 Nov 13;69(45):1675-1680.

24.  Lockdowns Do Not Control the Coronavirus: The Evidence. The American Institute For Economic Research. Dec 19th, 2020.

25.  Lovett, I. Fentanyl Has Spread West and Overdoses Are Surging. Wall Street Journal. April 15th, 2021.

26.  Mikovits, J. The Case Against Mask: Ten Reasons Why Mask Use Should be Limited. Aug 18th, 2020.

27.  Rabin, Roni Caryn. "U.S. Suicides Declined Over All in 2020 but May Have Risen Among People of Color." The New York Times. The New York Times, April 15, 2021. https://www.nytimes.com/2021/04/15/health/coronavirus-suicide-cdc.html.

28.  Rebillot, K. COVID Webinar Series (TRANSCRIPT): Robert Redfield, MD. https://www.buckinstitute.org/covid-webinar-series-transcript-robert-redfield-md/

29.  Rudd RA, Aleshire N, Zibbell JE, Gladden RM. Increases in Drug

and Opioid Overdose Deaths--United States, 2000-2014. MMWR
Morb Mortal Wkly Rep. 2016 Jan 1;64(50-51):1378-82.

30. Sakamoto H, Ishikane M, Ghaznavi C, Ueda P. Assessment of Suicide in Japan During the COVID-19 Pandemic vs Previous Years. JAMA Netw Open. 2021;4(2):e2037378.

31. Schippers, Michaéla C. "For the Greater Good? The Devastating Ripple Effects of the Covid-19 Crisis." Frontiers. Frontiers, September 9, 2020. https://www.frontiersin.org/articles/10.3389/fpsyg.2020.577740/full.

32. Van Hoof, E. Lockdown is the worlds biggest psychological experiment - and we will pay the price. Apr 9th, 2020. World Economic Forum. https://www.weforum.org/agenda/2020/04/this-is-the-psychological-side-of-the-covid-19-pandemic-that-were-ignoring/

33. Wasserman I.M. The impact of epidemic, war, prohibition and media on suicide: United States, 1910–1920. Behav. 1992;22:240-254.

34. Weiner, S. COVID-19 and the opioid crisis: When a pandemic and an epidemic collide. American Association of Medical Colleges. July 27, 2020.

35. Young, S., Smout,A. UK's Johnson warns lockdown, not vaccines, behind drop in COVID deaths. Reuters. April 13th, 2021.

36. Youngminds organization. Coronavirus: Impact on young people with mental health needs Survey 4: February 2021. www.youngminds.org.uk

37. Yrondi A, et al. FondaMental Advanced Centers of Expertise in Resistant Depression (FACE-DR), Courtet P, El-Hage W, Aouizerate B; List of FondaMental Advanced Centre of Expertise (FACE-DR) collaborators; FACE-DR Clinical Sites and Principal Collaborators in France. Childhood Trauma increases suicidal behaviour in a treatment-resistant depression population: a FACE-DR report. J Psychiatr Res. 2021 Mar;135:20-27.

**Chapter 5**

1. AACAP Suicide in children and teens [Internet]. Academy of Child and Adolescent Psychiatry. [cited 2020 Aug 28]., https://www.aacap.org/AACAP/Families_and_Youth/Facts_for_Families/FFF-Guide/Teen-Suicide-010.aspx (2018, December 16, 2020).

2. Admon LK, Dalton VK, Kolenic GE, Ettner SL, et al. Trends in Suicidality 1 Year Before and After Birth Among Commercially Insured Childbearing Individuals in the United States, 2006-2017. JAMA Psychiatry. 2020.

3. Anderson, M., & Jiang, J. (2018). Teens, social media & technology 2018. Pew Research Center, 31, 2018.

4. Ting, S. A., Sullivan, A. F., Boudreaux, E. D., Miller, I., & Camargo Jr, C. A. (2012). Trends in US emergency department visits for attempted suicide and self-inflicted injury, 1993–2008. General hospital psychiatry, 34(5), 557-565.

5. Berkeley, L., Kim, J. CDC warns Congress of 'significant public health consequences' if schools don't reopen in the fall. July 31st, 2020. https://www.cnbc.com/2020/07/31/cdc-warns-congress-of-significant-public-

health-consequences-if-schools-dont-reopen-in-the-fall.html

6. Bremner, J. U.S. Alcohol Sales Increase 55 Percent in One Week Amid Coronavirus Pandemic. Apr 1st, 2020. https://www.newsweek.com/ us-alcohol-sales-increase-55-percent-one-week-amid-coronavirus-pandemic-1495510

7. Buglewicz, J. Child Psychiatrists Warn That The Pandemic May Be Driving Up Kids' Suicide Risk. National Public Radio. Feb 2nd, 2021. https://www.npr.org/sections/health-shots/2021/02/02/962060105/ child-psychiatrists-warn-that-the-pandemic-may-be-driving-up-kids-suicide-risk.

8. Burke, M. Maine teen dies by suicide after struggling to cope with pandemic, father says. Dec 8th, 2020. https://www.nbcnews.com/news/us-news/ teen-dies-suicide-after-struggling-cope-pandemic-father-says-n1250442

9. Campo-Flores, A. Florida Schools Reopened Without Becoming Covid-19 Superspreaders. Wall Street Journal. March 17th, 2021.

10. Carballo, JJ, Llorente, C, Kehrmann, L,. Psychosocial risk factors for suicidality in children and adolescents. Eur Child Adolesc Psychiatry 2020; 29(6): 759–776.

11. Chatterjee, R. Child Psychiatrists Warn That The Pandemic May Be Driving Up Kids' Suicide Risk. NPR. Feb 2nd, 2021.

12. CRITICAL ISSUES IN POLICING SERIES. An Occupational Risk: What Every Police Agency Should Do To Prevent Suicide Among Its Officers. Police Executive Research Forum. October 2019.

13. Danbeck, J. Preliminary autopsy concludes Kodie Dutcher died from pharmacologic suicide. July 9th, 2020. https://www.nbc15.com/2020/07/09/ preliminary-autopsy-concludes-kodie-dutcher-died-from-pharmacologic-suicide/

14. DeGering, N., Bartlett, I. Bold plan to enhance mental and behavioral health begins in the Intermountain West. ABC4 News. Oct 26th, 2020. https://www.abc4.com/gtu/gtu-sponsor/ bold-plan-to-enhance-mental-and-behavioral-health-begins-in-the-intermountain-west/

15. Dennis EL,et al. Altered white matter microstructural organization in posttraumatic stress disorder across 3047 adults: results from the PGC-ENIGMA PTSD consortium. Mol Psychiatry. 2019 Dec 19.

16. DeVille DC, Whalen D, Breslin FJ, et al. Prevalence and Family-Related Factors Associated With Suicidal Ideation, Suicide Attempts, and Self-injury in Children Aged 9 to 10 Years. JAMA Netw Open. 2020;3(2):e1920956.

17. Encinas, C. Youth suicides up in Arizona; nearly 30% include Pima County. Nov 10th, 2020. https://www.kgun9.com/news/local-news/ youth-suicides-up-in-arizona-nearly-30-include-pima-county

18. Everytown – For Gun Safety. The Rise of Firearm Suicide Among Young Americans. Oct 10th, 2020. https://everytownresearch.org/ report/the-rise-of-firearm-suicide-among-young-americans/

19. Feder A, Murrough JW. Ketamine for post-traumatic stress

disorder. JAMA Psychiatry. 2015;72(1):95.

20. Feder A, Parides MK, Murrough JW, et al. Efficacy of intravenous ketamine for treatment of chronic post-traumatic stress disorder. JAMA Psychiatry. 2014;71(6):681–688.

21. Friedman, N. Locked-Down Teens Stay Up All Night, Sleep All Day. Wall Street Journal. May 22, 2020.

22. Gandhi, M. Noble, J. The Pandemic's Toll on Teen Mental Health. The CDC tried to spark a panic about Covid hospitalizations while ignoring the real crisis. Wall Street Journal. June 10th, 2021.

23. Green, Erica. Surge of Student Suicides Pushes Las Vegas Schools to Reopen. New York Times. January 24th, 2021. https://www.nytimes.com/2021/01/24/us/politics/student-suicides-nevada-coronavirus.html

24. Guessoum, SB, Lachal, J, Radjack, R. Adolescent psychiatric disorders during the COVID-19 pandemic and lockdown. Psychiatry Res 2020; 291: 113264.

25. Haas, Ann P et al. "Suicide and suicide risk in lesbian, gay, bisexual, and transgender populations: review and recommendations." Journal of homosexuality vol. 58,1 (2011): 10-51.

26. Hansotte E, Payne SI, Babich SM. Positive postpartum depression screening practices and subsequent mental health treatment for low-income women in Western countries: a systematic literature review. Public Health Rev. 2017 Jan 31;38:3.

27. Hayden Hunstable Website / https://www.youtube.com/watch?v=VJTHFhVyyqI.

28. Hermann, Peter. Two officers who helped fight the Capitol mob died by suicide. Many more are hurting. The Washington Post. Feb 12th, 2021.

29. Hill RM, Rufino K, Kurian S, Saxena J, Saxena K, Williams L. Suicide Ideation and Attempts in a Pediatric Emergency Department Before and During COVID-19. Pediatrics. 2021 Mar;147(3):e2020029280.

30. Hinduja S, Patchin JW. Bullying Beyond the Schoolyard: Preventing and Responding to Cyberbullying. Thousand Oaks, CA: Sage Publications; 2009.

31. Janiri D, Doucet GE, Pompili M, Sani G, Luna B, Brent DA, Frangou S. Risk and protective factors for childhood suicidality: a US population-based study. Lancet Psychiatry. 2020 Apr;7(4):317-326.

32. Kim, C. Orange County Family Shares Teen Suicide Story as Pandemic Warning to Other Parents. Jan 19th, 2021. https://www.nbclosangeles.com/news/local/orange-county-family-shares-teen-suicide-story-as-pandemic-warning-to-other-parents/2509206/

33. Krause, Adam J et al. "The sleep-deprived human brain." Nature reviews. Neuroscience vol. 18,7 (2017): 404-418.

34. Kingkade, T and Chuck, E. Suicidal thoughts are increasing in young kids, experts say. It began before the pandemic. NBC news. Apr 8th, 2021. https://www.nbcnews.com/news/us-news/suicidal-thoughts-are-increasing-young-kids-experts-say-it-began-n1263347

35. Khmara, D. With teen suicide on the rise, Tucson educators struggle

to prioritize mental health counselors skip student meetings to cover
for staff who are sick, exposed to COVID. Dec 27th, 2020.

36.  Knoll, C. With an E.R. Doctor's Suicide, The Virus Claims Another Life (New York-Presbyterian Allen Hospital doctor Lorna M. Breen). The New York times. Jul 12th, 2020.

37.  Lapidus KA, Levitch CF, Perez AM, Brallier JW, Parides MK, Soleimani L, Feder A, Iosifescu DV, Charney DS, Murrough JW. A randomized controlled trial of intranasal ketamine in major depressive disorder. Biol Psychiatry. 2014 Dec 15;76(12):970-6.

38.  Lee, J. Mental health effects of school closures during COVID-19. Lancet Child Adolesc Health 2020; 4(6): 421.

39.  Lee. M. Hillary Clinton's misleading claim that 'numerous surveys' show veterans are satisfied with VA medical care. The Washington Post. Nov 2nd, 2015.

40.  Lemle, Russell B. "Veterans, Firearms, and Suicide: Safe Storage Prevention Policy and the PREVENTS Roadmap." Federal practitioner: for the health care professionals of the VA, DoD, and PHS vol. 37,9 (2020).

41.  Lewiecki, E Michael, and Sara A Miller. "Suicide, guns, and public policy." American journal of public health vol. 103,1 (2013): 27-31.

42.  Lindahl V, Pearson JL, Colpe L. Prevalence of suicidality during pregnancy and the postpartum. Arch Womens Ment Health. 2005 Jun;8(2):77-87.

43.  Lapidus KA, Levitch CF, Perez AM, Brallier JW, Parides MK, Soleimani L, Feder A, Iosifescu DV, Charney DS, Murrough JW. A randomized controlled trial of intranasal ketamine in major depressive disorder. Biol Psychiatry. 2014 Dec 15;76(12):970-6.

44.  Liu, JJ, Bao, Y, Huang, X, Shi, J, Lu, L. Mental health considerations for children quarantined because of COVID-19. Lancet Child Adolesc Health 2020; 4(5): 347–349.

45.  Ma Jia Hui. Prophylactic use of ketamine reduces postpartum depression in Chinese women undergoing cesarean section - Psychiatry Research 279 (2019)252-258.

46.  Manorama Online 173 child suicides in Kerala since lockdown, stress forced most. On Manorama [Internet]. [cited 2020 Nov 16], https://www.onmanorama.com/news/kerala/2020/10/26/children-death-by-suicide-on-the-rise-in-kerala.html (2020, December 16, 2020).

47.  McGhee LL, Maani CV, Garza TH, Slater TM, Petz LN, Fowler M. The intraoperative administration of ketamine to burned US service members does not increase the incidence of post-traumatic stress disorder. Mil Med. 2014;179(8):41.

48.  McLoughlin, Larisa T et al. "Neurobiological underpinnings of cyberbullying: A pilot functional magnetic resonance imaging study." Human brain mapping vol. 41,6 (2020): 1495-1504.

49.  Morin CM, Carrier J. The acute effects of the COVID-19 pandemic on insomnia and psychological symptoms. Sleep Med. 2021;77:346-347.

50.  National Child Mortality Database. Briefing published: Child suicide during COVID-19. Jul 9, 2020.

51. O'Hara AF, Violanti JM, Levenson RL Jr, Clark RG Sr. National police suicide estimates: web surveillance study III. Int J Emerg Ment Health. 2013;15(1):31-8.

52. Papst, C. 'He just gave up' - School shutdown drives Baltimore County teen to depression, suicide. Nov 23rd, 2020. https://foxbaltimore.com/news/project-baltimore/he-just-gave-up-school-shutdown-baltimore-county-teen-impact

53. Pirkis J, et al. Suicide trends in the early months of the COVID-19 pandemic: an interrupted time-series analysis of preliminary data from 21 countries. Lancet Psychiatry. 2021 Jul;8(7):579-588.

54. Phillips, James G et al. "Instances of online suicide, the law and potential solutions." Psychiatry, psychology, and law: an interdisciplinary journal of the Australian and New Zealand Association of Psychiatry, Psychology and Law vol. 26,3 423-440. 17 Feb. 2019.

55. Rasmussen KG. Ketamine for post-traumatic stress disorder. JAMA Psychiatry. 2015;72(1):94–95.

56. Ravindran, Chandru et al. "Association of Suicide Risk With Transition to Civilian Life Among US Military Service Members." JAMA network open vol. 3,9 e2016261. Sep 1st,. 2020.

57. Sheftall, Arielle H et al. "Suicide in Elementary School-Aged Children and Early Adolescents." Pediatrics vol. 138,4 (2016): e20160436.

58. Siegel, M. COVID: The Politics of Fear and the Power of Science Hardcover. Turner Publishing. Oct 13th, 2020.

59. Suicide Awareness Voices of Education (SAVE), 2020.

60. Taylor, Kate. Gun sales boomed in 2020 with background checks hitting record highs as millions of people bought guns for the first time. Business Insider Magazine. Jan 15th, 2021.

61. The Times of India Increasing suicidal tendency among children during lockdown in Kerala; Over 60 end lives since March 25—Times of India. The Times of India [Internet]. Thiruvananthapuram. [cited 2020 Sep 14], https://timesofindia.indiatimes.com/home/education/news/increasing-suicidal-tendency-among-children-during-lockdown-in-kerala-over-60-end-lives-since-march-25/articleshow/76924011.cms (2020, December 16, 2020).

62. The Hindu Student suicides rising, 28 lives lost every day. The Hindu [Internet]. [cited 2020 Aug 27], https://www.thehindu.com/news/national/student-suicides-rising-28-lives-lost-every-day/article30685085.ece (2020, December 16, 2020).

63. The Independent Coronavirus lockdown may have led to increased child suicides, new report warns. The Independent [Internet]. [cited 2020 Nov 17], https://www.independent.co.uk/news/health/coronavirus-uk-child-suicide-mental-health-nhs-a9617671.html (2020, December 16, 2020).

64. https://tucson.com/news/local/with-teen-suicide-on-the-rise-tucson-educators-struggle-to-prioritize-mental-health/article_7db1b000-c0aa-5066-931f-fed3443e0102.html

65. Walker ER, McGee RE, Druss BG. Mortality in mental disorders

and global disease burden implications: a systematic review and meta-analysis. JAMA Psychiatry. 2015 Apr;72(4):334-41.

66.   Walker, Matthew P et al. "Sleep and the time course of motor skill learning." Learning & memory (Cold Spring Harbor, N.Y.) vol. 10,4 (2003): 275-84.

67.   Wang, A. Another sheriff's deputy dies by suicide. This time, his boss wants people to talk about it. The Washington Post. Aug 2nd, 2017.

68.   Wang, G, Zhang, Y, Zhao, J, Zhang, J, Jiang, F. Mitigate the effects of home confinement on children during the COVID-19 outbreak. Lancet 2020; 395(10228): 945–947.

69.   Warden D. Military TBI during the Iraq and Afghanistan wars. J Head Trauma Rehabil. 2006 Sep-Oct;21(5):398-402.

70.   Weber, Garret et al. "Case Report of Subanesthetic Intravenous Ketamine Infusion for the Treatment of Neuropathic Pain and Depression with Suicidal Features in a Pediatric Patient." Case reports in anesthesiology vol. 2018 9375910. 26 Jul. 2018.

**Chapter 6**

1.    Arsenault-Lapierre G, Kim C, Turecki G. Psychiatric diagnoses in 3275 suicides: a meta-analysis. BMC Psychiatry. 2004 Nov 4; 4():37.

2.    Bolwig TG, Fink M. Electrotherapy for melancholia: The pioneering contributions of Benjamin Franklin and Giovanni Aldini. J ECT. 2009.

3.    Brink A. Depression and loss: A theme in Robert Burton's "Anatomy of Melancholy" (1621). Can J Psychiatry. 1979;24(8):767-72.

4.    Busch, K. Eta al. "Clinical Correlates of Inpatient Suicide." The Journal of Clinical Psychiatry 64, no. 1 (Jan 2003): 14-9.

5.    Buss, D. M. (2015). Evolutionary psychology: The new science of the mind.

6.    https://www.businessinsider.com/gun-sales-boom-2020-background-checks-hit-record-highs-2021-1.

7.    Center for Substance Abuse Treatment. Addressing Suicidal Thoughts and Behaviors in Substance Abuse Treatment. Rockville (MD): Substance Abuse and Mental Health Services Administration (US); 2009. (Treatment Improvement Protocol (TIP) Series, No. 50.) Part 1, Chapter 1, Addressing Suicidal Thoughts and Behaviors in Substance Abuse Treatment: Information You Need To Know. Available from: https://www.ncbi.nlm.nih.gov/books/

8.    Dawkins, Richard. The Selfish Gene. Oxford: Oxford University Press, 1989.

9.    Franklin, J. C., Fox, K. R., Franklin, C. R., Kleiman, E. M., Ribeiro, J. D., Jaroszewski, A. C., Hooley, J. M., & Nock, M. K. (2016). A brief mobile app reduces nonsuicidal and suicidal self-injury: Evidence from three randomized controlled trials. Journal of Consulting and Clinical Psychology, 84(6), 544–557.

10.   Gladwell, Malcolm. 2019. Talking to strangers: what we should know about the people we don't know.

11.   Glenn, J. et al. "Suicide and Self-Injury-Related Implicit

Cognition: A Large-Scale Examination and Replication." Journal of Abnormal Psychology 126, no. 2 (Feb 2017): 199-211.

12. Gureje, O., Oladeji, B., Hwang, I. et al. Parental psychopathology and the risk of suicidal behavior in their offspring: results from the World Mental Health surveys. Mol Psychiatry 16, 1221–1233, 2011.

13. Hampson, N. "U.S. Mortality Due to Carbon Monoxide Poisoning, 1999-2014. Accidental and Intentional Deaths." Annals of the American Thoracic Society 13, no. 10 (Oct 2016): 1768-74.

14. Harmer B, Lee S, Duong TVH, Saadabadi A. Suicidal Ideation. 2021 Apr 28. In: StatPearls [Internet]. Treasure Island (FL): StatPearls Publishing; Jan 2021.

15. Hillhouse TM, Porter JH. A brief history of the development of antidepressant drugs: from monoamines to glutamate. Exp Clin Psychopharmacol. 2015 Feb;23(1):1-21.

16. Jacobson, N, Nemesure, M. Using Artificial Intelligence to Predict Change in Depression and Anxiety Symptoms in a Digital Intervention: Evidence from a Transdiagnostic Randomized Controlled Trial, Psychiatry Research, Volume 295, 2021.

17. Lapierre CB, Schwegler AF, Labauve BJ. Posttraumatic stress and depression symptoms in soldiers returning from combat operations in Iraq and Afghanistan. J Trauma Stress. 2007 Dec;20(6):933-43.

18. McGowan PO, Sasaki A, D'Alessio AC, Dymov S, Labonté B, Szyf M, Turecki G, Meaney MJ. Epigenetic regulation of the glucocorticoid receptor in human brain associates with childhood abuse. Nat Neurosci. 2009 Mar;12(3):342-8.

19. Meng-Jie Wang, et al. How Common is Cyberbullying Among Adults? Gender, Ethnic, and Age Differences in the Prevalence of Cyberbullying. Cyberpsychology, Behavior, and Social Networking 2019 22:11, 736-741.

20. Millard C. A History of Self-Harm in Britain: A Genealogy of Cutting and Overdosing. Basingstoke (UK): Palgrave Macmillan; 2015. Chapter 1, Early Twentieth-Century Self-Harm: Cut Throats, General and Mental Medicine. Available from: https://www.ncbi.nlm.nih.gov/books/NBK333534/

21. Millard, C., & Ougrin, D. (2017). Narrative Matters: Self-harm in Britain post-1945: the evolution of new diagnostic category. Child and adolescent mental health, 22(3), 175–176.

22. Mock, C. N., Grossman, D. C., Mulder, D., Stewart, C., & Koepsell, T. S. Health care utilization as a marker for suicidal behavior on an American Indian reservation. 11, Journal of General Internal Medicine, (1996):519–524.

23. Nock, M, et al. Jennifer M Park, Christine T Finn, Tara L Deliberto, Halina J Dour, and Mahzarin R Banaji. "Measuring the Suicidal Mind: Implicit Cognition Predicts Suicidal Behavior." Psychological science 21, no. 4 (Apr 2010): 511-7.

24. Musu, L. Zhang, A., Wang, K., Zhang, J., Oudekerk, B. Indicators of School Crime and Safety: 2018. National Center for Education Statistic. April 17th, 2019.

25. Nesse, R. Good Reasons for Bad Feelings: Insights from the Frontier of Evolutionary Psychiatry. Feb 12, 2019.

26. Thiessen,D.D. Mechanism specific approaches in behavior genetics, p. 91.

27. Ngui, Emmanuel M et al. "Mental disorders, health inequalities and ethics: A global perspective." International review of psychiatry (Abingdon, England) vol. 22,3 (2010): 235-44.

28. Tipton CM. The history of "Exercise Is Medicine" in ancient civilizations. Adv Physiol Educ. 2014;38(2):109–117.

29. Rachel Swan, R. Golden Gate Bridge Suicides Nets Delayed 2-Years, As People Keep Jumping. San Francisco Chronicle, Dec 12th, 2019.

30. "Saving Lives at the Golden Gate Bridge." Golden Gate Bridge Highway & Transportation District, accessed March 1, 2021, https://www.goldengatebridgenet.org.

31. Schechner, S., Olson, P. Artificial Intelligence, Facial Recognition Face Curbs in New EU Proposal. Wall Street Journal. April 21st, 2021.

32. Shrier, Abigail. 2020. Irreversible damage: the transgender craze seducing our daughters. https://rbdigital.rbdigital.com.

33. Swan, R. "Golden Gate Bridge Suicide Nets Delayed Two Years, as People Keep Jumping." Local, San Francisco Chronicle, 2019. https://www.sfchronicle.com/bayarea/article/Golden-Gate-Bridge-suicide-nets-delayed-two-14900278.php.

34. Tjaden, P., Thoennes, N. Full Report of the Prevalence, Incidence, and Consequences of Violence Against Women. Findings From the National Violence Against Women Survey. Nov 2000 NCJ 183781.

35. Van Orden, Kimberly A et al. "The interpersonal theory of suicide." Psychological review vol. 117,2 (2010): 575-600.

36. Voracek M, Loibl LM. Genetics of suicide: a systematic review of twin studies. Wien Klin Wochenschr. 2007;119(15-16):463-75.

37. Wilson ST, Chesin M, Fertuck E, Keilp J, Brodsky B, Mann JJ, Sönmez CC, Benjamin-Phillips C, Stanley B. Heart rate variability and suicidal behavior. Psychiatry Res. 2016 Jun 30;240:241-247.

38. Wilson, T. "Know Thyself." Perspectives on Psychological Science 4, no. 4 (Jul 2009): 384-9. https://doi.org/10.1111/j.1745-6924.2009.01143.x.

## Chapter 7

1. Admon LK, Dalton VK, Kolenic GE, Ettner SL, et al. Trends in Suicidality 1 Year Before and After Birth Among Commercially Insured Childbearing Individuals in the United States, 2006-2017. JAMA Psychiatry. 2020.

2. Admon R, Milad MR, Hendler T. A causal model of post-traumatic stress disorder: disentangling predisposed from acquired neural abnormalities. Trends Cogn Sci. 2013 Jul;17(7):337-47.

3. Anderson G, Maes M. Schizophrenia: linking prenatal infection to cytokines, the tryptophan catabolite (TRYCAT) pathway, NMDA

receptor hypofunction, neurodevelopment and neuroprogression. Prog Neuropsychopharmacol Biol Psychiatry. 2013 Apr 5;42:5-19.

4.   Andrade C. Ketamine for Depression, 1: Clinical Summary of Issues Related to Efficacy, Adverse Effects, and Mechanism of Action. J Clin Psychiatry. 2017 Apr;78(4):e415-e419.

5.   Bahr, Rebecca et al. "Intranasal Esketamine (SpravatoTM) for Use in Treatment-Resistant Depression In Conjunction With an Oral Antidepressant." P & T: a peer-reviewed journal for formulary management vol. 44,6 (2019): 340-375.

6.   Ballard ED, Luckenbaugh DA, Richards EM, et al. Assessing measures of suicidal ideation in clinical trials with a rapid-acting antidepressant. J Psychiatr Res. 2015;68:68-73.

7.   Ballard ED, Ionescu DF, Vande Voort JL, et al. Improvement in suicidal ideation after ketamine infusion: relationship to reductions in depression and anxiety. J Psychiatr Res. 2014;58:161-166.

8.   Berman RM, Cappiello A, Anand A, Oren DA, Heninger GR, Charney DS, Krystal JH. Antidepressant effects of ketamine in depressed patients. Biol Psychiatry. 2000 Feb 15;47(4):351-4.

9.   Brown GK, Ten Have T, Henriques GR, Xie SX, Hollander JE, Beck AT. Cognitive therapy for the prevention of suicide attempts: a randomized controlled trial. JAMA. 2005 Aug 3;294(5):563-70.

10.  Calabrese, L. Titrated Serial Ketamine Infusions Stop Outpatient Suicidality and Avert ER Visits and Hospitalizations. Int J Psychiatr Res. 2019; 2(6): 1-12.

11.  Cope, NA., Arnold, DE. Depression: Doctors Are Turning to Ketamine for Treatment. Time Magazine. July 27th, 2017.

12.  Dockrill, P. Oral Ketamine Experiment Reduces Suicidal Thoughts in Over Two-Thirds of Patients. Feb 9th, 2021. https://www.sciencealert.com/oral-ketamine-experiment-reduces-suicidal-thoughts-in-over-two-thirds-of-patients

13.  Domany Y, Shelton RC, McCullumsmith CB. Ketamine for acute suicidal ideation. An emergency department intervention: a randomized, double-blind, placebo-controlled, proof-of-concept trial Depress Anxiet. Nov 16th, 2019.

14.  Fan W, Yang H, Sun Y, Zhang J, Li G, Zheng Y, Liu Y. Ketamine rapidly relieves acute suicidal ideation in cancer patients: a randomized controlled clinical trial. Oncotarget. 2017 Jan 10;8(2):2356-2360.

15.  Fazel, S., Runeson, B. "Suicide." New England Journal of Medicine 382, no. 3 (Jan 16, 2020): 266-74.

16.  Feder A, Parides MK, Murrough JW, Perez AM, Morgan JE, Saxena S, Kirkwood K, Aan Het Rot M, Lapidus KA, Wan LB, Iosifescu D, Charney DS. Efficacy of intravenous ketamine for treatment of chronic posttraumatic stress disorder: a randomized clinical trial. JAMA Psychiatry. 2014 Jun;71(6):681-8.

17.  Feder A, Nestler EJ, Charney DS. Psychobiology and molecular genetics of resilience. Nat Rev Neurosci. 2009 Jun;10(6):446-57.

18.  Grande LA. Sublingual Ketamine for Rapid Relief of Suicidal Ideation. Prim Care Companion CNS Disord. 2017 Mar 9;19(2).

19.  Guglielminotti J, Li G. Exposure to General Anesthesia for Cesarean Delivery and Odds of Severe Postpartum Depression Requiring Hospitalization. Anesth Analg. 2020 Nov;131(5):1421-1429.

20.  Haapanen, L. Ketamine Safe for Acutely Suicidal Patients in the Emergency Department Setting. Dec 5th, 2019. https://www.psychiatryadvisor.com/home/depression-advisor/ketamine-safe-for-acutely-suicidal-patients-in-the-emergency-department-setting/

21.  Hansotte, E., Payne, S.I. & Babich, S.M. Positive postpartum depression screening practices and subsequent mental health treatment for low-income women in Western countries: a systematic literature review. Public Health Rev 38, 3, 2017.

22.  Haroon E, Miller AH. Inflammation Effects on Brain Glutamate in Depression: Mechanistic Considerations and Treatment Implications. Curr Top Behav Neurosci. 2017;31:173-198.

23.  Hui, M. Prophylactic use of ketamine reduces postpartum depression in Chinese women undergoing cesarean section. Psychiatry Research 279 (2019)252-258.

24.  Hyde, S. Ketamine for Depression. 2015.

25.  Ionescu, Dawn F et al. "Ketamine-Associated Brain Changes: A Review of the Neuroimaging Literature." Harvard review of psychiatry vol. 26,6 (2018): 320-339.

26.  Jansen, K. Ketamine: Dreams and Realities. Published by MAPS [Multidisciplinary Association for Psychedelic Studies] www.maps.org. 2004.

27.  Krupitsky EM, Grinenko AY. Ketamine psychedelic therapy (KPT): a review of the results of ten years of research. J Psychoactive Drugs. 1997 Apr-Jun;29(2):165-83.

28.  Lapidus KA, Levitch CF, Perez AM, Brallier JW, Parides MK, Soleimani L, Feder A, Iosifescu DV, Charney DS, Murrough JW. A randomized controlled trial of intranasal ketamine in major depressive disorder. Biol Psychiatry. 2014 Dec 15;76(12):970-6.

29.  Laursen TM, Munk-Olsen T, Vestergaard M. Life expectancy and cardiovascular mortality in persons with schizophrenia. Curr Opin Psychiatry. 2012 Mar;25(2):83-8.

30.  Laursen TM, Plana-Ripoll O, Andersen PK, et al. Cause-specific life years lost among persons diagnosed with schizophrenia: is it getting better or worse? Schizophr Res. 2019;206:284-290.

31.  Li L, Vlisides PE. Ketamine: 50 Years of Modulating the Mind. Front Hum Neurosci. 2016;10:612. Published 2016 Nov 29.

32.  Lindahl V, Pearson JL, Colpe L. Prevalence of suicidality during pregnancy and the postpartum. Arch Womens Ment Health. 2005 Jun;8(2):77-87.

33.  Luke G. A preliminary naturalistic study of low-dose Ketamine for depression and suicide in the emergency department. Int J of Neuropsychopharmacology 2011.

34.  Mandavilli, A. The Biggest Monster' Is Spreading. And It's Not the Coronavirus. The New York Times. Aug 3rd, 2020.

35.  Matveychuk D, Thomas RK, Swainson J, et al. Ketamine as an antidepressant: overview of its mechanisms of action and potential predictive biomarkers. Ther Adv Psychopharmacol. 2020;10:2045125320916657. Published 2020 May 11.

36.  McGhee LL, Maani CV, Garza TH, Slater TM, Petz LN, Fowler M. The intraoperative administration of ketamine to burned U.S. service members does not increase the incidence of post-traumatic stress disorder. Mil Med. 2014 Aug;179(8 Suppl):41-6.

37.  McIntyre RS, Carvalho IP, Lui LMW, Majeed A, Masand PS, Gill H, Rodrigues NB, Lipsitz O, Coles AC, Lee Y, Tamura JK, Iacobucci M, Phan L, Nasri F, Singhal N, Wong ER, Subramaniapillai M, Mansur R, Ho R, Lam RW, Rosenblat JD. The effect of intravenous, intranasal, and oral ketamine in mood disorders: A meta-analysis. J Affect Disord. 2020 Nov 1;276:576-584.

38.  Mead GE, Morley W, Campbell P, Greig CA, McMurdo M, Lawlor DA. Exercise for depression. Cochrane Database Syst Rev. 2008 Oct 8;(4):CD004366. doi: 10.1002/14651858.CD004366.pub3. Update in: Cochrane Database Syst Rev. 2009;(3):CD004366. PMID: 18843656.

39.  Mo H, Campbell MJ, Fertel BS, Lam SW, Wells EJ, Casserly E, Meldon SW. Ketamine Safety and Use in the Emergency Department for Pain and Agitation/Delirium: A Health System Experience. West J Emerg Med. 2020 Jan 27;21(2):272-281.

40.  Murrough JW, Soleimani L, DeWilde KE, Collins KA, Lapidus KA, Iacoviello BM, Lener M, Kautz M, Kim J, Stern JB, Price RB, Perez AM, Brallier JW, Rodriguez GJ, Goodman WK, Iosifescu DV, Charney DS. Ketamine for rapid reduction of suicidal ideation: a randomized controlled trial. Psychol Med. 2015 Dec;45(16):3571-80.

41.  Murrough JW, Iosifescu DV, Chang LC, Al Jurdi RK, Green CE, Perez AM, Iqbal S, Pillemer S, Foulkes A, Shah A, Charney DS, Mathew SJ. Antidepressant efficacy of ketamine in treatment-resistant major depression: a two-site randomized controlled trial. Am J Psychiatry. 2013 Oct;170(10):1134-42.

42.  Murrough JW. A randomized controlled trial of intranasal ketamine in major depressive disorder. Biol Psychiatry. 2014 Dec 15;76(12):970-6.

43.  Niesters M, Aarts L, Sarton E, Dahan A. Influence of ketamine and morphine on descending pain modulation in chronic pain patients: a randomized placebo-controlled cross-over proof-of-concept study. Br J Anaesth. 2013 Jun;110(6):1010-6.

44.  Parikh, T. Walkup, J. The Future of Ketamine in the Treatment of Teen Depression. The American Journal of Psychiatry. Apr 1st, 2021.

45.  Perry BI, Stochl J, Upthegrove R, Zammit S, Wareham N, Langenberg C, Winpenny E, Dunger D, Jones PB, Khandaker GM. Longitudinal Trends in Childhood Insulin Levels and Body Mass Index and Associations With Risks of Psychosis and Depression in Young Adults. JAMA Psychiatry. 2021 Apr 1;78(4):416-425.

46.  Phillips JL, Norris S, Talbot J, Hatchard T, Ortiz A, Birmingham M, Owoeye O, Batten LA, Blier P. Single and repeated ketamine infusions for reduction of suicidal ideation in treatment-resistant depression. Neuropsychopharmacology. 2020 Mar;45(4):606-612.

47.  Pigott, H Edmund. "The STAR*D Trial: It Is Time to Reexamine the Clinical Beliefs That Guide the Treatment of Major Depression." Canadian journal of psychiatry. Revue canadienne de psychiatrie vol. 60,1 (2015): 9-13.

48.  Pradhan B, Rossi G. Combining Ketamine, Brain Stimulation (rTMS) and Mindfulness Therapy (TIMBER) for Opioid Addiction. Cureus. 2020;12(11):e11798. Published 2020 Nov 30.

49.  Reinstatler L, Youssef NA. Ketamine as a potential treatment for suicidal ideation: a systematic review of the literature. Drugs R D. 2015 Mar;15(1):37-43.

50.  Sakai C, Mackie TI, Shetgiri R, Franzen S, Partap A, Flores G, Leslie LK. Mental health beliefs and barriers to accessing mental health services in youth aging out of foster care. Acad Pediatr. 2014 Nov-Dec;14(6):565-73.

51.  Sarnyai, Zoltán, and Christopher M Palmer. "Ketogenic Therapy in Serious Mental Illness: Emerging Evidence." The international journal of neuropsychopharmacology vol. 23,7 (2020): 434-439.

52.  Song XM, Li JG, Wang YL, et al. Effects of ketamine on proinflammatory cytokines and nuclear factor kappaB in polymicrobial sepsis rats. World J Gastroenterol. 2006;12(45):7350-7354.

53.  Ting SA, Sullivan AF, Miller I, Espinola JA, Allen MH, Camargo CA Jr, Boudreaux ED; Emergency Department Safety and Follow-up Evaluation (ED-SAFE) Investigators. Multicenter study of predictors of suicide screening in emergency departments. Acad Emerg Med. 2012 Feb;19(2):239-43.

54.  Velasquez-Manoff, M. Ketamine Stirs Up Hope-and Controversy- as a Depression Drug. Wired Magazine. May 8th, 2018.

55.  Stix, G. From Club to Clinic: Physicians Push Off-Label Ketamine as Rapid Depression Treatment, Part 1 – Scientific American Blog Network. Sept 11th, 2013. https://blogs.scientificamerican.com/talking-back/from-club-to-clinic-physicians-push-off-label-ketamine-as-rapid-depression-treatment-part-1/

56.  Vietnam studies, Department of the Army, 1973. https://history.army.mil/html/bookshelves/collect/vn-studies.html

57.  Wang J, Goffer Y, Xu D, et al. A single subanesthetic dose of ketamine relieves depression-like behaviors induced by neuropathic pain in rats. Anesthesiology. 2011;115(4):812-821.

58.  Wilkinson ST, Wright D, Fasula MK, Fenton L, Griepp M, Ostroff RB, Sanacora G. Cognitive Behavior Therapy May Sustain Antidepressant Effects of Intravenous Ketamine in Treatment-Resistant Depression. Psychother Psychosom. 2017;86(3):162-167.

59.  Wilkinson ST, Katz RB, Toprak M, Webler R, Ostroff RB, Sanacora G. Acute and Longer-Term Outcomes Using Ketamine as a Clinical Treatment at the Yale Psychiatric Hospital. J Clin Psychiatry. 2018 Jul 24;79(4):17m11731.

60.  Wilkinson, Samuel T et al. "The Effect of a Single Dose of Intravenous Ketamine on Suicidal Ideation: A Systematic Review and Individual Participant Data Meta-Analysis." The American journal of psychiatry vol. 175,2 (2018): 150-158.

61. Wolfson, P. Hartelius, G. The Ketamine Papers: Science, Therapy, and Transformation. Multidisciplinary Association for Psychedelic Studies. November 1, 2016.

62. Zarate, C. A. Jr et al. A randomized trial of an N-methyl-d-aspartate antagonist in treatment-resistant major depression. Arch. Gen. Psychiatry 63, 856–864, 2006.

## Chapter 8

1. Clements, J. A., Nimmo, W. S. & Grant, I. S. Bioavailability, pharmacokinetics, and analgesic activity of ketamine in humans. J. Pharm. Sci. 71, 539–542 (1982).

2. Deyama S, Duman RS. Neurotrophic mechanisms underlying the rapid and sustained antidepressant actions of ketamine. Pharmacol Biochem Behav. 2020;188:172837.

3. Fragoso YD, et al. Severe depression, suicide attempts, and ideation during the use of interferon beta by patients with multiple sclerosis. Clin Neuropharmacol. 2010;33(6):312–6.

4. Haroon E, Miller AH. Inflammation Effects on Brain Glutamate in Depression: Mechanistic Considerations and Treatment Implications. Curr Top Behav Neurosci. 2017;31:173-198.

5. Janelidze S, et al. Cytokine levels in the blood may distinguish suicide attempters from depressed patients. Brain Behav Immun. 2011;25(2):335–9.

6. Khan MS, Wu GWY, Reus VI, et al. Low serum brain-derived neurotrophic factor is associated with suicidal ideation in major depressive disorder. Psychiatry Res. 2019;273:108-113.

7. Li, N. et al. mTOR-dependent synapse formation underlies the rapid antidepressant effects of NMDA antagonists. Science 329, 959–964 (2010).

8. Li Y, Shen R, Wen G, et al. Effects of ketamine on levels of inflammatory cytokines IL-6, IL-1beta, and TNF-alpha in the hippocampus of mice following acute or chronic administration. Front Pharmacol. 2017;8:139.

9. Lindqvist D, et al. Interleukin-6 is elevated in the cerebrospinal fluid of suicide attempters and related to symptom severity. Biol Psychiatry. 2009;66(3):287–92.

10. Ma XC, Liu P, Zhang XL, Jiang WH, Jia M, Wang CX, Dong YY, Dang YH, Gao CG. Intranasal Delivery of Recombinant AAV Containing BDNF Fused with HA2TAT: a Potential Promising Therapy Strategy for Major Depressive Disorder. Sci Rep. 2016 Mar 3;6:22404.

11. Nuland, Sherwin M.D., How Electroshock Therapy Changed Me. 2001. https://www.ted.com/talks/sherwin_nuland_how_electroshock_therapy_changed_me?language=en

12. Palmer CM, Gilbert-Jaramillo J, Westman EC. The ketogenic diet and remission of psychotic symptoms in schizophrenia: Two case studies. Schizophr Res. 2019 Jun;208:439-440.

13. Perry BI, McIntosh G, Weich S, Singh S, Rees K. The association between first-episode psychosis and abnormal glycaemic control: systematic review and meta-analysis. Lancet Psychiatry. 2016 Nov;3(11):1049-1058.

14. Perry BI, Upthegrove R, Thompson A, Marwaha S, Zammit S, Singh SP, Khandaker G. Dysglycaemia, Inflammation and Psychosis: Findings From the UK ALSPAC Birth Cohort. Schizophr Bull. 2019 Mar 7;45(2):330-338.

15. Pribish A, Wood N, Kalava A. A Review of Nonanesthetic Uses of Ketamine. Anesthesiol Res Pract. 2020;2020:5798285. Published 2020 Apr 1.

16. Raison CL, et al. Activation of central nervous system inflammatory pathways by interferon-alpha: relationship to monoamines and depression. Biol Psychiatry. 2009;65(4):296–303.

17. Reinstatler, L. Youssef, NA. Ketamine as a Potential Treatment for Suicidal Ideation: A Systematic Review of the Literature Drugs R D (2015) 15:37–43.

18. Sacher, J et al., Serotonergic Modulation of Intrinsic Functional Connectivity. Curr Bio., 24 (19), 2314-19, 2014.

19. Sattar Y, Wilson J, Khan A M, et al. (May 18, 2018) A Review of the Mechanism of Antagonism of N-methyl-D-aspartate Receptor by Ketamine in Treatment-resistant Depression. Cureus 10(5): e2652.

20. Shanahan, Catherine, Deep Nutrition: Why Your Genes Need Traditional Food. 2017.

21. Steiner J, et al. Immunological aspects in the neurobiology of suicide: elevated microglial density in schizophrenia and depression is associated with suicide. J Psychiatr Res. 2008; 42(2):151–7.

22. Strasburger SE, Bhimani PM, Kaabe JH, et al. What is the mechanism of Ketamine's rapid-onset antidepressant effect? A concise overview of the surprisingly large number of possibilities. J Clin Pharm Ther. 2017;42:147–154.

23. Wang N, Yu HY, Shen XF, et al. The rapid antidepressant effect of ketamine in rats is associated with down-regulation of pro-inflammatory cytokines in the hippocampus. Ups J Med Sci. 2015;120(4):241-248.

24. Wichers MC, et al. IDO and interferon-alpha-induced depressive symptoms: a shift in hypothesis from tryptophan depletion to neurotoxicity. Mol Psychiatry. 2005;10(6):538–44.

25. Wolfson M.D., Phil. The Ketamine Papers: Science, Therapy, and Transformation (p. 172). Multidisciplinary Association for Psychedelic Studies.

26. Yang, Y., Cui, Y., Sang, K. et al. Ketamine blocks bursting in the lateral habenula to rapidly relieve depression. Nature 554, 317–322 (2018).

27. Yang X, Yang Q, Wang X, et al. MicroRNA expression profile and functional analysis reveal that miR-206 is a critical novel gene for the expression of BDNF induced by ketamine. Neuromolecular Med. 2014;16:594–605.

28. Zarate, C. A. Jr et al. A randomized trial of an N-methyl-d-aspartate antagonist in treatment-resistant major depression. Arch. Gen. Psychiatry 63, 856–864 (2006).

Chapter 9

1. Bhojani, B. A RECOVERY STORY: After Every Available Option Was Exhausted, Ketamine Has Enabled Her Life to Resume. March 31st, 2019. Brain & Behavior Magazine. https://www.bbrfoundation.org/blog/recovery-story-after-every-available-option-was-exhausted-ketamine-has-enabled-her-life-resume

2. Feifel D, Dadiomov D, C Lee K. Safety of Repeated Administration of Parenteral Ketamine for Depression. Pharmaceuticals (Basel). 2020 Jul 13;13(7):151.

3. Feifel D, Malcolm B, Boggie D, Lee K. Low-dose ketamine for treatment resistant depression in an academic clinical practice setting. J Affect Disord. 2017 Oct 15;221:283-288.

4. Godoy DA, Badenes R, Pelosi P, Robba C. Ketamine in acute phase of severe traumatic brain injury "an old drug for new uses?". Crit Care. 2021 Jan 6;25(1):19.

5. Green SM, Clem KJ, Rothrock SG. Ketamine safety profile in the developing world: survey of practitioners. Acad Emerg Med. 1996 Jun;3(6):598-604.

6. Ketamine is revolutionizing antidepressant research, but we still don't know how it works (acs.org). Accessed June 14th, 2021.

7. Hamilton Pharmacopeia. Ketamine; Realms and Realities. 2017.

8. Hamilton, J (2018, June). From Chaos To Calm: A Life Changed by Ketamine. National Public Radio. https://www.npr.org/sections/health-shots/2018/06/04/615671405/from-chaos-to-calm-a-life-changed-by-ketamine

9. Hyde, Dr. Stephen J.. Ketamine for Depression. 2015. Kindle Edition.

10. Ketalar package insert. KETALAR (ketamine hydrochloride) injection (fda.gov).

11. Kenneth Rein, author of Life and Death classifies the NDE 5 stage continuum:

12. Jansen, Karl M.D., Ph.D., Ketamine: Dreams and Realities. 2004. Multidiciplinary Association for Psychedelic Studies (MAPS).

13. Ketamine Advocacy Network. [(accessed on 24 May 2019)]; Available online: http://www.ketamineadvocacynetwork.org/mission-and-vision/

14. Koch, C. Tales of the Dying Brain. Scientific American 322, 6, 70-75 (June 2020)

**Chapter 10**

1. Davis, AK, Barret FS, May DG, et al. Effects of Psilocybin-Assisted Therapy on Major Depressive Disorder: A Randomized Clinical Trial. JAMA Psychiatry. 2021;78(5):481-489.

2. Feifel D, Malcolm B, Boggie D, Lee K. Low-dose ketamine for treatment resistant depression in an academic clinical practice setting. J Affect Disord. 2017 Oct 15;221:283-288.

3. David Feifel M.D. https://www.kadimanp.com/

4. Hodges, Linda M.D. Thinking of Starting a Ketamine Clinic? 2019.

5. Hyde, Dr. Stephen J. Ketamine for Depression. 2015.

6. Ketamine Advocacy Network. www.ketamineadvocacynetwork.org

7.    www.Ketaminefund.org

8.    Mathew SJ, Murrough JW, aan het Rot M, Collins KA, Reich DL, Charney
      DS. Riluzole for relapse prevention following intravenous ketamine in
      treatment-resistant depression: a pilot randomized, placebo-controlled
      continuation trial. Int J Neuropsychopharmacol. 2010 Feb;13(1):71-82.

9.    Social Inpact Foundation

10.   Wolfson M.D., Phil. The Ketamine Papers: Science, Therapy, and Transformation
      (pp. 293-294). Multidisciplinary Association for Psychedelic Studies, 2016.

# INDEX

Made in the USA
Columbia, SC
30 October 2021